Welcome to Preferred.

CONTENTS

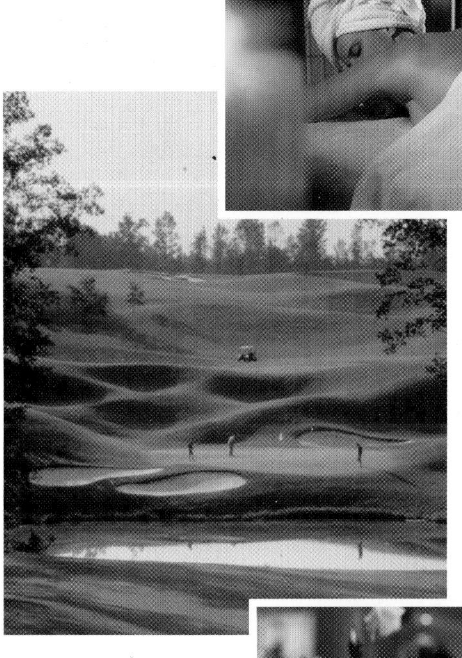

WELCOME TO PREFERRED

WORLDWIDE LOCATIONS

Preferred's hotels and resorts are divided into the following regions: The Americas, Caribbean, Europe, Africa and Asia. Within each of these sections, the hotels are listed alphabetically: first, by country; second, by state/province; third, by city; and last, by hotel name. For quick reference, refer to the index beginning on page 180.

CHAMPAGNE
PERRIER JOUËT
Unforgettable.
PERRIER JOUËT
CUVEE
BELLE EPOQUE
CHAMPAGNE
BRUT

CONTENTS

ISBN 0-9726208-0-X

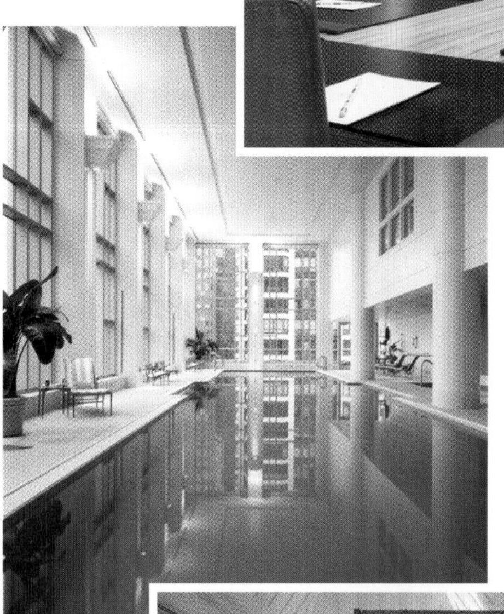

MEETING PLANNING, SPAS & RESORT HOTEL AMENITIES

INDEXES

For quick reference to a hotel by city, region or name, please use one of the indexes below:

CONTACT US

To learn more about Preferred's partnerships and programs, complete and return the reply card located on the inside back cover or forward your inquiry to:

Preferred Hotels® & Resorts Worldwide
311 South Wacker Drive, Suite 1900
Chicago, Illinois 60606 U.S.A.
Tel: +1.312.913.0400 Fax: +1.312.913.0444
info@preferredhotels.com
www.preferredhotels.com

CHECK IN

to the world of haute hotels

The more you want out of your holiday, the more you need a Virtuoso travel specialist. We know the world and all the ways for you to discover it.

As our client, hundreds of the world's finest hotels, resorts, spas and lodges will roll out the red carpet for you. We'll get you into the right hotel, in the right room, with the right view . . . when others can't. You'll also enjoy upgrades and special amenities or services at no additional cost — all as our guest.

The world awaits.
Call your Virtuoso travel specialist today and let us take you there. 800-401-4274

VIRTUOSO
SPECIALISTS IN THE ART OF TRAVEL

PREFERRED ADVISORY BOARD

Photographed from left to right:

MR. STEPHAN J.A.B. STOKKERMANS
Commercial Director
Grand Hotel Huis ter Duin
Amsterdam/Noordwijk aan Zee,
The Netherlands

MR. ANTON PIRINGER
Vice President of Hospitality
Vail Resorts, Inc.
Vail, Colorado U.S.A.

MR. DAVID G. BENTON, Chairperson
Vice President & General Manager
The Rittenhouse Hotel
Philadelphia, Pennsylvania U.S.A.

MR. WILLIAM J. OTTO
President
Marcus Hotels and Resorts
Milwaukee, Wisconsin U.S.A.

MR. ROBERT M. CORNELL
Managing Director
Preferred Hotels & Resorts Worldwide
Chicago, Illinois U.S.A.

MR. SAYED M. SALEH
President & General Manager
The Orchards
Williamstown, Massachusetts U.S.A.

MR. EDWARD R. (Peter) CASS
President & CEO
IndeCorp Corporation
Chicago, Illinois U.S.A.

MR. PETER AEBY
Chairman of the Board
IndeCorp Corporation
Chicago, Illinois U.S.A.

A LETTER FROM THE MANAGING DIRECTOR

Dear Guest:

I am frequently asked, what makes a hotel a Preferred hotel and how are Preferred hotels different? Having stayed at nearly all of our hotels personally, I can testify that there is a core commitment within our ranks to maintain a positive attitude toward service. We refer to this as the "Preferred Experience." Each of our 1,600 standards and practices is adopted by our hotels in a special way that takes maximum advantage of their unique locations and facilities. Be it a bustling city center or a remote resort destination, you can be assured that you will receive the same unsurpassed service and response to all of your needs during your stay.

The 116 Preferred hotels presented in this directory have been selected through an extensive process of evaluations, on-site inspections and random service checks to assure that they meet Preferred's Standards of Excellence™ quality assurance program. They have all earned the privilege of displaying the coveted Preferred plaque on their door, which is a sign of their commitment to the highest standards. As each hotel is re-inspected every year, these standards must be maintained at all times.

As we endeavor to improve the overall level of quality and options for guests of Preferred, we continue to add new hotels that meet the rigorous Preferred standards. By the same token, if a hotel is unable or unwilling to operate at the high standards we require, they are asked to leave Preferred. To make sure that our hotels meet these requirements, Preferred's field inspectors assume the identity of regular hotel guests in order to anonymously check each item and verify their application to the needs of today's discerning travelers. In fact, frequent users of Preferred are often the best judges of whether or not a hotel belongs among our ranks, and we welcome your comments and suggestions at any time.

How many Preferred Hotels have you experienced, and which are your favorites? Please let us know by visiting our Web site, www.preferredhotels.com, and filling out your own evaluation. Your comments will be considered when it is time to select Preferred's Hotel of the Year.

We look forward to welcoming you, and welcoming you back very soon.

Sincerely,

Robert M. Cornell
Managing Director

Preferred Hotels® & Resorts Worldwide
Tel: +1.312.913.0400 Fax: +1.312.913.0444
E-mail: info@preferredhotels.com

Estimado Huésped,

A lo largo de las páginas de este directorio, nos complace presentarle 116 de los mejores y más lujosos hoteles y resorts independientes del mundo. Cada uno de estos hoteles ha sido seleccionado mediante un extenso proceso de evaluaciones, inspecciones in situ y comprobaciones del personal realizadas al azar para asegurar que satisfacen las normas del programa de garantía de calidad Preferred's Standards of Excellence™.

Todos ellos se han ganado el privilegio de colocar en sus puertas la codiciada placa Preferred, que es un símbolo de su compromiso con las más exigentes normas de calidad. Y dado que cada uno de estos hoteles recibe una inspección todos los años, estas normas de calidad deben mantenerse en todo momento.

A menudo me preguntan qué requiere un hotel para pertenecer a Preferred y en qué se diferencian de los demás. Después de haber estado en casi todos nuestros hoteles personalmente, puedo atestiguar que existe un compromiso claro entre nuestro personal para mantener una actitud positiva hacia el servicio. Nos referimos a esto como la "Experiencia Preferred." Nuestros hoteles adoptan cada uno de nuestros 1.600 criterios y prácticas de un modo especial, logrando sacar el máximo partido a sus exclusivas instalaciones. Tanto si se trata del centro de una bulliciosa ciudad, como de un destino vacacional remoto, puede estar convencido de que recibirá el mismo servicio y la misma respuesta inigualables para todo lo que necesite durante su estancia.

Si usted es un usuario habitual de los Hoteles Preferred, percibirá algunos cambios entre nuestros miembros cada año, ya que fomentamos el nivel general de la calidad de los productos que ofrecemos añadiendo nuevos miembros. De la misma manera, si un hotel no puede o no está dispuesto a trabajar con los niveles de calidad que solicitamos, les pedimos que abandonen Preferred. Para asegurarnos de que nuestros hoteles cumplen estos requisitos, los inspectores de Preferred asumen la identidad de huéspedes de hotel para comprobar, de forma anónima, cada uno de los elementos y verificar su aplicación en respecto a las necesidades de los exigentes viajeros de hoy en día. De hecho, los huéspedes habituales de Preferred suelen ser los mejores jueces a la hora de determinar si un hotel puede figurar entre nuestros miembros, por lo que le agradecemos cualquier comentario o sugerencia que desee realizar.

¿En cuántos Hoteles Preferred se ha alojado y cuál es su favorito? Por favor, háganoslo saber visitando nuestra página web www.preferredhotels.com y completando su propia hoja de evaluación. Cuando llegue el momento, sus comentarios serán tenidos en cuenta a la hora de seleccionar el Hotel Preferred del Año.

Deseamos darle la bienvenida o volver a dársela muy pronto.

Atentamente,

Director General

Preferred Hotels® & Resorts Worldwide
Tel: +1 312 913 0400 Fax: +1 312 913 0444
Correo electrónico: info@preferredhotels.com

Sehr geehrter Gast,

wir freuen uns, Ihnen auf den Seiten dieses Verzeichnisses 116 der besten unabhängigen Luxushotels und Resorts weltweit präsentieren zu dürfen. Jedes Hotel wurde umfangreichen Bewertungsverfahren, Vor-Ort-Prüfungen und stichprobenartigen Prüfungen des Services unterworfen, um zu gewährleisten, dass sie die Qualitätsrichtlinien des Preferred's Standards of Excellence™ erfüllen. Sie haben sich alle das Privileg verdient, die begehrte Preferred Plakette an ihrer Tür zu tragen, die ein Zeichen der Verpflichtung zu höchstem Standard in sich trägt, und da sich jedes dieser Hotels Jahr für Jahr wieder der Prüfung unterziehen muss, bleibt dieser Standard stets gewahrt.

Ich werde häufig gefragt, was ein Preferred Hotel ausmacht und wie sie sich von anderen unterscheiden. Nachdem ich in nahezu allen unserer Hotels persönlich gewohnt habe, kann ich bestätigen, dass es in unseren Reihen eine Kernverpflichtung gibt, mit einer positiven Einstellung unseren Service anzubieten. Wir nennen dies die "Bevorzugte Erfahrung". Jede unserer 1.600 Richtlinien und Praktiken wird in unseren Hotels individuell angewandt, um den maximalen Nutzen aus einer jeden Einrichtung zu ziehen. Ganz egal, ob es sich nun um ein geschäftiges Stadtzentrum oder ein entlegenes Resort handelt, Sie können versichert sein, dass Sie während Ihres Aufenthalts überall denselben unübertroffenen Service und dieselbe uneingeschränkte Beachtung antreffen werden.

Wenn Sie bereits regelmäßig in unseren Preferred Hotels wohnen, werden Sie jedes Jahr einige Veränderungen bei unseren Mitgliedern feststellen, da wir bestrebt sind, das Gesamtniveau an Produktqualität stetig zu verbessern, indem wir neue Mitglieder aufnehmen. Aus dem gleichen Grund fordern wir auch von jenen Hotels die Preferred Mitgliedschaft zurück, die nicht bereit oder in der Lage sind, auf diesem hohen Niveau zu arbeiten. Um sicher zu stellen, dass unsere Hotels auch diese Anforderungen erfüllen, senden wir regelmäßig Inspektoren als normale Hotelgäste in unsere Hotels, um unerkannt sowohl jeden Punkt als auch die Hingabe für die Bedürfnisse des kritischen Reisenden von heute zu überprüfen. Tatsache ist, dass häufige Gäste in unseren Preferred Hotels am Besten beurteilen können, ob ein Hotel noch in unsere Reihen gehört. Teilen Sie uns daher Ihre Kommentare und Vorschläge jederzeit mit.

Wie viele Preferred Hotels haben Sie bereits kennen gelernt? Welches ist Ihr Lieblingshotel? Besuchen Sie unsere Web-Seite unter www.preferredhotels.com, und geben Sie Ihre eigene Bewertung ab. Ihre Eingaben finden dann bei der Wahl des Preferred Hotels des Jahres Berücksichtigung.

Wir freuen uns auf Ihren Besuch, und wir freuen uns darauf, Sie schon bald wieder bei uns begrüßen zu dürfen.

Mit freundlichen Grüßen,

Robert M. Cornell
Managing Director

Preferred Hotels® & Resorts Worldwide
Tel: +1 312 913 0400 Fax: +1 312 913 0444
E-Mail: info@preferredhotels.com

Gentile Ospite,

Nelle pagine di questo elenco siamo lieti di presentare 116 alberghi di lusso tra i migliori migliori al mondo. Ogni albergo è stato selezionato con un rigoroso processo di ispezioni e controlli di servizi che sono eseguiti a sorpresa per assicurare che siano conformi al programma di garanzia di qualità Preferred's Standards of Excellence™. Tutti i nostri alberghi hanno ottenuto il privilegio di esporre all'ingresso l'ambita placca "Preferred", che garantisca il loro impegno a mantenere gli standard di servizi più elevati e, dal momento che ciascun albergo viene ispezionato ogni anno, gli standard sono mantenuti costantemente.

Mi viene chiesto spesso qual'è la differenza sostanziale di un "Preferred Hotel." Avendo soggiornato personalmente presso quasi tutti gli alberghi della nostra associazione, posso testimoniare che alla base esiste l'impegno di mantenere un' eccellente qualità di servizio a tutti i livelli. Ciò che definiamo la "Preferred Experience". Ciascuno dei nostri 1.600 standard e norme viene adottato dai nostri alberghi in modo personalizzato per poter trarre il massimo vantaggio. Sia che si tratti di un albergo ubicato in centro citta' o di una remota destinazione turistica, si può essere certi che, durante ogni soggiorno, si riceve lo stesso insuperabile servizio e la stessa impeccabile risposta a tutte le esigenze.

Se lei è un cliente abituale dei Preferred Hotels e Resorts, avrà avuto modo di constatare le modifiche annuali apportate all'elenco degli appartenenti alla nostra associazione, in quanto il nostro impegno è di migliorare il livello complessivo della qualità del prodotto offerto e ciò viene effettuato aggiungendo nuovi membri. Per lo stesso principio se un albergo non è in grado di o non è disposto a operare seguendo i nostri alti standard qualitativi, gli viene revocata l'appartenenza. Per garantire che i nostri alberghi siano sempre conformi ai requisiti, valutiamo constantemente i livelli di servizio usando ispettori locali che assumono l'identità di regolari ospiti al fine di controllare in modo anonimo ciascun punto e verificarne l'applicazione alle necessità degli esigenti viaggiatori di oggi. Di fatto, gli ospiti abituali dei Preferred Hotels sono spesso i miglior giudici della qualità di un albetrgo e sono in grado di stabilire se lo stesso debba far parte o meno della nostra associazione. Le saremo grati se volesse fornirci un suo commento o suggerimento.

Quante volte ha sperimentato l'accoglienza di un Preferred Hotel e quale ha preferito? Ci invii un suo comment scritto, visitando il nostro sito www.preferredhotels.com e compilando il modulo di valutazione in linea. I suoi suggerimenti verranno presi in grande considerazione al momento di selezionare il migliore tra i Preferred's Hotel dell'anno.

Attendiamo con ansia la possibilità di ospitarla e di vederla ritornare molto presto.

Cordialmente,

Robert M. Cornell
Amministratore delegato

Preferred Hotels® & Resorts Worldwide
Tel: +1 312 913 0400 Fax: +1 312 913 0444
Posta elettronica: info@preferredhotels.com

Cher Hôte,

Vous découvrirez, en parcourant ce guide, une sélection mondiale de 116 Hôtels et Resorts indépendants répertoriés et reconnus comme les plus luxueux hôtels au monde.

Afin de vous garantir que chaque Hôtel réponde au mieux aux normes d'excellence du programme d'assurance qualité intitulé "Preferred's Standards of Excellence™" chaque établissement a fait l'objet de plusieurs contrôles stricts d'évaluation, des inspections sur site ainsi que des contrôles inopinés des prestations de service.

Ces 116 hôtels et resorts ont tous mérité le privilège de pouvoir apposer la plaque tant convoitée de "Preferred" ce qui implique également un signe d'engagement dans le terme de respect des standards de service les plus élevés. En effet, chaque année chaque hôtel ou resort fait à nouveau l'objet d'une nouvelle inspection qui permet de mesurer et de valider les promesses d'engagement de qualité.

Je suis souvent questionné sur ce qui caractérise un hôtel "Preferred" et en quoi ces hôtels sont-ils différents? Ayant séjourné personnellement dans la quasi totalité de nos hôtels, je puis attester qu'il s'affirme, au sein de chaque établissement, une forte volonté de délivrer la meilleure prestation de services qui soit! Nous appelons cela "l'Expérience Preferred."

Chacun des 1600 points de contrôle est adopté par nos hôtels ce qui optimise encore le caractère exceptionnel et unique de leurs infrastructures. Que l'hôtel soit situé en centre ville ou dans une destination de villégiature plus retirée, vous pouvez être certain que vous bénéficierez du même service inégalé et des mêmes attentions tout au long de séjour.

Si vous êtes un habitué des Hôtels Preferred, vous constaterez, d'une année sur l'autre, quelques mouvements dans la liste de nos affiliés. D'une part nous accueillons bien-sûr certains nouveaux hôtels au sein de notre Collection, mais aussi malheureusement il nous arrive de nous séparer de certains hôtels qui n'ont pu satisfaire aux critères de qualité requis par Preferred Hotels & Resorts.

Afin d'une part de nous assurer que nos hôtels répondent aux critères exigés et d'autre part de vérifier aussi leur correspondance avec les attentes des voyageurs actuels, des "inspecteurs terrain Preferred" prennent l'identité d'un client et contrôlent anonymement chaque élément du service.

En réalité, les clients habitués de "Preferred" sont nos meilleurs "juges." C'est la raison pour laquelle vos commentaires et vos suggestions sont et seront toujours les bienvenus.

Dans combien d'Hôtels "Preferred" avez-vous séjourné et lequel est votre favori? Merci de nous faire part de votre opinion. Vos commentaires seront pris en compte lorsqu'il s'agira de choisir l'Hôtel "Preferred" de l'année. Visitez donc notre site web www.preferredhotels.com et prenez quelques instants pour remplir le formulaire destiné à cet effet.

Nous sommes dans l'attente de vous accueillir, et ce, très prochainement.

Sincèrement,

Robert M. Cornell
Directeur général

Preferred Hotels® & Resorts Worldwide
Tél: +1 312 913 0400 Fax: +1 312 913 0444
E-mail: info@preferredhotels.com

尊敬的宾客：

在本目录的各页中，我们很高兴为您呈上世界上 116 间独立拥有的豪华城市和度假胜地酒店。每间酒店的选择，都经过了一个广泛的评估、现场检查和随机服务核查过程，以保证它们符合“首选优秀标准”(Preferred’s Standards of Excellence™) 的品质保证计划。它们都获得了在其大门上贴上令人景仰的“首选酒店”铭牌的特权，这是它们对最高标准承诺的象征，而且，每间酒店每年都要接受重新检查，以确保始终如一的优秀标准。

经常有人问我，一间酒店如何能成为“首选”酒店，它有何不同？当我亲自在大部分的“首选”酒店住过后，我可以证实，在我们等级评定中，有一个对保持积极服务态度的核心承诺，我们将之称为“首选经验”(Preferred Experience)。我们的 1600 个标准和惯例中的每一项内容，都被我们的酒店以充分利用其独特设施优势的特殊方式加以采纳。无论是一个热闹非凡的国际都市，抑或是一个遥远的度假胜地，我可以向您保证，在您逗留期间，您都可以获得同等的出色服务，同时您的所有需求都将得到满足。

如果您是“首选酒店”的常客，您将会注意到，我们的成员每年都会有一些变化，这是因为我们以努力通过增加新成员来改进产品质量的整体水平。基于同样原因，如果一间酒店未能或不愿意按我们要求的高标准经营，我们将会要求其退出首选名单。为了确保我们的酒店符合这些要求，“首选酒店”的现场检查员会以酒店常客的身份，匿名检查每个项目，并考察其是否能满足当今富辩识能力的游客之需求。事实上，首选酒店的常客通常是判断一间酒店是否达到我们的等级的最佳评判人，因此我们随时欢迎您提出宝贵意见和建议。

您体验过多少间首选酒店？您最喜欢哪一间？请访问我们的网站 www.preferredhotels.com 并填写您的评估表格，将您的意见告诉我们。在评选本年度的“首选酒店”时，我们将会考虑您的意见。

我们热切期待着欢迎您，并希望您在不久的将来再次光临。

诚挚的，

Robert M. Cornell
常务董事
Preferred Hotels® & Resorts Worldwide
电话：+1 312 913 0400 传真：+1 312 913 0444
电子邮件：info@preferredhotels.com

お客様各位

拝啓

同封の加盟ホテル名鑑では、世界各地にある独立系高級ホテルとリゾートホテルの中でも最高級である116 軒の宿泊施設をご案内しております。各ホテルのどれもが、査定、現地での点検、サービスの無作為検査といった幅広い選別プロセスを経て選び抜かれ、Preferred（プリファード）のStandards of Excellence™品質保証プログラムに確実に適合しております。これら厳選されたホテルは、業界で羨望の的であるPreferredのプレートをホテルのドアに飾っておく栄誉を勝ち取ってまいりました。また、このプレートはホテル側の最高級の水準への飽くなき追求の証でもあり、再検査は毎年1つ1つのホテルに対して行われるため、これらの水準は対象ホテルで常に保たれている必要があります。

さて、加盟ホテルの資格条件や他のホテルとの違いについてよく質問を頂くことがあります。加盟ホテルのほぼすべてに宿泊したことがある私自身の経験から申し上げますと、加盟ホテルにはサービスに対する前向きの姿勢を常に保とうという基本的な取り組みがあるのが共通事項だと言えると思います。これを当社では「プリファード・エクスペリエンス(プリファードホテルに宿泊することで選び抜かれたサービスの実体験)」と呼んでおります。当社設定の1,600にのぼる基準や慣行の1つ1つが加盟ホテルのユニークな宿泊施設を最大限生かせるような特別な方法で実施されています。宿泊ホテルが街の中心地にあろうと遠く離れたリゾート地にあろうと、ご滞在中は他の追随を許さないサービスとお客様のあらゆるニーズに対しての対応をどこのホテルへ行っても同じように受けることが期待できます。

お客様がPreferred Hotels(プリファード・ホテル)によくお泊りでしたら、加盟ホテルに毎年変更があることにもうお気付きだと思います。これも新規会員ホテルを加盟させ全体の商品価値の向上を当社では常に努めているからです。同様に当社が要求する高水準な品質の提供が出来なかったり、また提供する意思がないホテルには、Preferredを退会するように求めます。こういった資格条件に加盟ホテルが適合しているかをチェックするため、Preferredの現地検査員は通常のホテル宿泊客のふりをしてホテル側に知られることなく各項目を点検し、現代のセンスの高いお客様の立場になって、ニーズに合っているかを確認します。加盟ホテルが当社のレベルに合っているかどうかは、Preferredをよくご利用のお客様の方がよくご存知だと思いますので、ご意見・ご感想をいつでもお待ちしております。

Preferred Hotelsのホテルには何軒お泊りになっていただきましたでしょうか。また、その中ではどれを一番お気に召したでしょうか。当社のホームページwww.preferredhotels.comにアクセスしお客様のご意見を是非お聞かせください。頂いたご意見はPreferredの「ホテル・オブ・ザ・イヤー」受賞を決定する際の参考にさせていただきます。

近い将来、お客様がお越しになるのを、また何度もご利用いただくのをお待ちしております。

敬具

Preferred Hotels® & Resorts Worldwide
マネジング・ディレクター
ロバート・M・コーネル
TEL：+1 312 913 0400　FAX：+1 312 913 0444
E-mail: rcornell@preferredhotels.com

PREFERRED'S STANDARDS OF EXCELLENCE™ PROGRAM

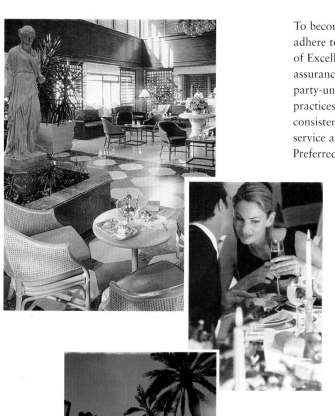

To become a Preferred member, hotels must adhere to Preferred's award-winning Standards of Excellence™ program, an exhaustive quality-assurance program that includes an annual, third-party-unannounced audit of 1,600 standards and practices. As a result of this unique program, guests consistently receive the highest levels of attentive service and luxurious accommodations at all Preferred hotels and resorts.

To ensure that the Preferred standards are current, several of our experienced hotel managers serve on the Quality Assurance Committee. The Quality Assurance Committee meets on a regular basis to discuss travel trends and developments that may affect our regular travelers.

Each year, refinements are made to our inspection checklist to reflect the needs of our guests, and hotels are notified to change their training programs to reflect any modifications.

If you have any ideas or suggestions on how our program can be further enhanced, please visit our Web site at www.preferredhotels.com and let us know your thoughts.

PREFERRED HOTELS & RESORTS SERVICES "ABOVE EXPECTATIONS"

As part of Preferred's Standards of Excellence™ quality-assurance program, our licensed quality assurance inspectors take special care to examine three categories of Preferred hotel amenities that you, our guests, have found very important:

FAMILY SERVICE AMENITIES

For travelers with infants and younger children, hotels displaying this icon welcome children and are prepared to offer such items as cribs, children's menus, games and baby-sitting services.

HEALTH AND FITNESS FACILITIES

For travelers who wish to maintain a fitness regimen while on the road, hotels displaying this icon provide supervised facilities with access to cardio-vascular equipment, resistance training equipment and free weights.

TELECOMMUNICATIONS

For travelers who wish to stay connected while on the road, hotels displaying this icon are equipped with telecommunications capabilities that allow travelers to conduct simultaneous voice and digital communications from their guestroom or a business center in the hotel.

THE CONFERENCE COLLECTION

Many Preferred hotels and resorts are specially equipped to handle meetings and conferences ranging in size from a board meeting of 10 to banquets for 1,000 persons. These hotels meet certain minimum standards specific to meeting and conference services, and therefore are designated with the Conference Collection icon. This special designation means that you can be confident that participating hotels have the experience and capabilities to provide professional services and amenities to meeting planners and attendees.

LEGEND

- Conference Collection
- Family Services
- Health and Fitness
- Internet and Telecommunications

PREFERRED PARTNERS

Preferred is committed to partnering with highly recognized brands to enhance the travel experience and bring more value to our guests. Our objective is to partner with prestigious brands that can enhance an already memorable experience — one that is as unique and distinct as each of our independently owned hotels and resorts.

Preferred maintains relationships with the following Marketing Partners:

UNITED
Mileage Plus®

Through Preferred's partnership with United Airlines Mileage Plus®, Mileage Plus members can earn 500 bonus miles per stay at all Preferred hotels and resorts. To qualify, please identify yourself as a United Mileage Plus member and provide your membership number at check-in.*

Alaska Airlines

Many Preferred hotels and resorts on the West Coast of North America are partners in Alaska Airlines' Mileage Plan program. Mileage Plan members can earn 500 miles per stay at any participating hotel or resort. To qualify, please identify yourself as an Alaska Airlines Mileage Plan member and provide your membership number at check-in. For a list of participating properties, please visit the Preferred Web site at www.preferredhotels.com.*

PERRIER-JOUËT

Preferred partners with this luxury Champagne brand, which is known worldwide for its consistency and style. As one of the most prestigious houses in Champagne and a top-selling champagne in the United States, Perrier-Jouët offers quality and individuality that are a natural fit for the discerning and sophisticated guests of Preferred Hotels® & Resorts Worldwide.

Cards

The American Express® Card is warmly welcomed at all Preferred hotels and resorts. No matter which Preferred hotel or resort you visit around the world, the American Express Card is one of the most recognized forms of payment.

Preferred partners with *USA Today* and AT&T to bring quality amenities and services to all of our business and leisure guests.

For up-to-date details on Preferred's new Marketing Partners, visit us at: www.preferredhotels.com

*If you are a member of more than one of the mentioned programs, points may be claimed in only one program per paid stay.

CELEBRATE LUXURY LIFESTYLE WITH *THE PREFERRED WAY* MAGAZINE

The Preferred Way magazine is a celebration of today's luxury lifestyle. Articles bring you, the Preferred guest, profiles on the world's best food and wine, fashion, events and, of course, a closer look at the properties of Preferred, the most distinctive luxury hotels and resorts in the world. *The Preferred Way,* published by Preferred Hotels® & Resorts Worldwide, is available in the guest rooms of every Preferred property worldwide. Please accept and enjoy your copy of *The Preferred Way* with our compliments. Journey *The Preferred Way.*

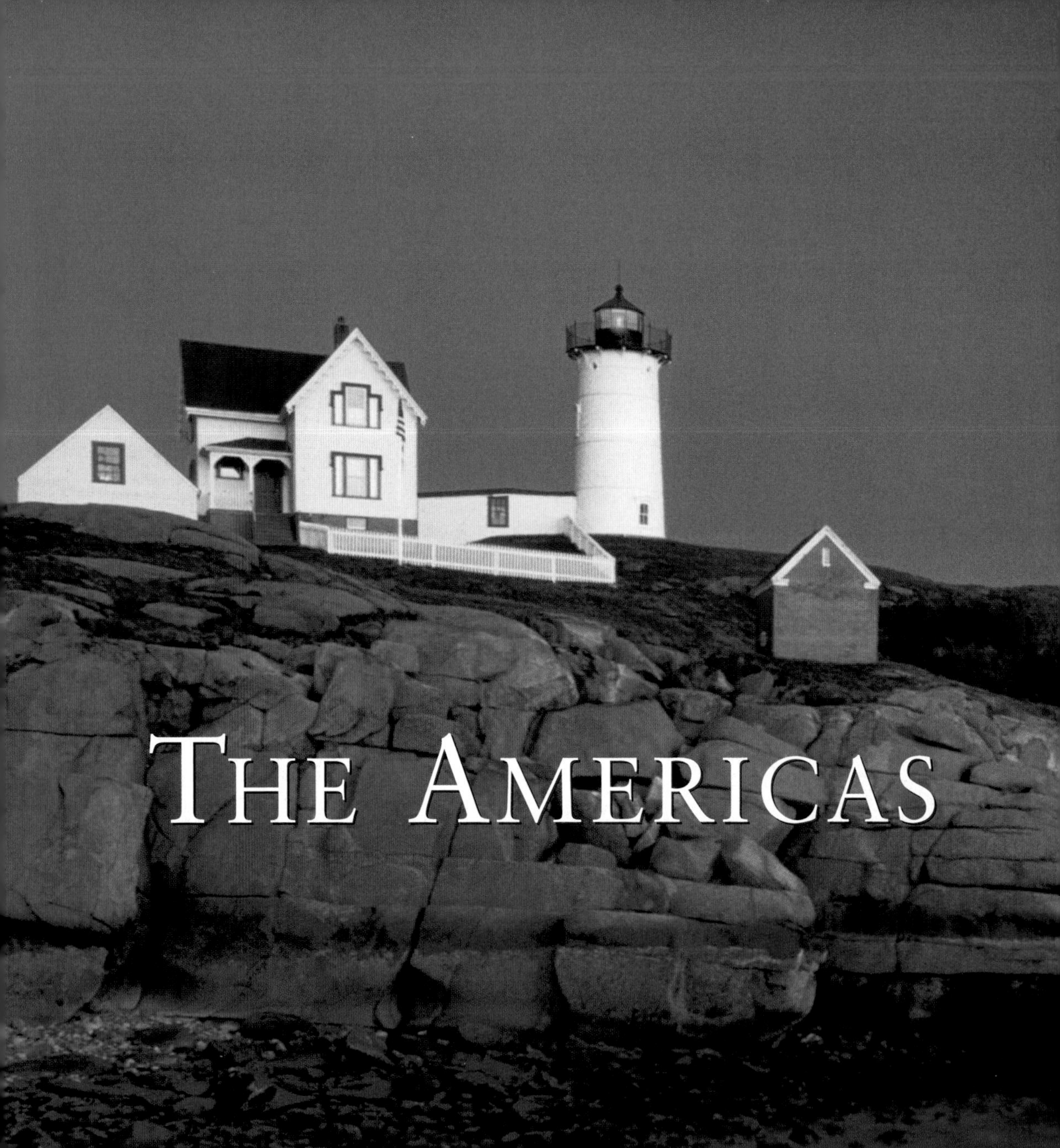
THE AMERICAS

The Americas

Opening Winter 2002

GRAN ESTANPLAZA SÃO PAULO

Newly built, this neoclassical palace features unique décor creating a warm and charming ambiance for each visitor. Guests can escape from the hustle and bustle of the contemporary business district that surrounds the hotel to this full-service, European-style luxury retreat. The hotel's neighborhood, surrounded by Berrini Avenue, is where most international companies have their Brazilian offices. The World Trade Center, shopping, restaurants and bars are available across the street. Guarulhos Intl. Airport: 22 miles/35 km, 40 minutes.

ACCOMMODATIONS: 209 total guestrooms, including 87 suites, each with three phones (two multi-line), data port, high-speed Internet access, voice mail, VCR available on request, newspaper, fax machine, safe, mini-bar, robes and hair dryer.

FACILITIES/SERVICES: Spa, concierge services, shoe shine, fitness center, dry cleaning and shops. Airline and car rental desk available.

BUSINESS SERVICES: On-site Business Center, secretarial and translating services available.

DINING: Two restaurants and bars provide the best of Brazilian and International cuisine and drinks.

MEETINGS: Total Meeting Rooms: 7 Total Sq. Ft.: 9,688 / Sq. M.: 900

RATES: USD 200.00 to 1,500.00; Corporate, Group, Package rates.

Mr. Angelo Donatti,
General Manager

Rua Arizona, 1517 - Brooklin Novo
São Paulo, Brazil 04567-003
Tel: +5511.3059.3279
Fax: +5511.3059.3289
Email: gran@estanplaza.com.br
www.estanplaza.com.br

Worldwide Reservations
www.preferredhotels.com
800.323.7500 U.S.A./Canada
00.800.3237.5001 Europe (UIFN)
Other areas: *See page 192*

METROPOLITAN HOTEL, VANCOUVER

ACCOMMODATIONS: 197 total guestrooms, including 16 suites, each with oversized marble bathrooms, soaker tubs, separate walk-in showers, Frette bathrobes, high-speed-broadband connectivity access, two dual-line phones, voice mail, newspaper, fully stocked bars and opening windows.

FACILITIES/SERVICES: Les Clefs d'Or Concierge, squash, indoor pool, whirlpool, saunas, massage therapy, downtown limousine service, fitness center, dry cleaning.

BUSINESS SERVICES: Business Center with translating services, high-speed broadband connectivity, video teleconferencing and audio-visual services.

DINING: "Diva at the Met" award-winning restaurant, lounge and patio, a celebrated local favorite offering Pacific Northwest originality.

MEETINGS: Total Meeting Rooms: 7 Total Sq. Ft.: 7,800 / Sq. M.: 726

RATES: CAD 229.00 to 399.00; Corporate, Group, Package rates.

Ms. Susan Gomez, General Manager

645 Howe Street
Vancouver, British Columbia V6C 2Y9, Canada
Tel: +1.604.687.1122
Fax: +1.604.689.7044
Email: reservations@metropolitan.com
www.metropolitan.com

An intimate refuge at the vibrant center of Vancouver's financial, shopping and entertainment districts. Guests are surrounded with classic contemporary styling and elegant décor in a cosmopolitan setting. Downtown, just steps from Pacific Centre, Queen Elizabeth Theatre and Robson Street shops. Vancouver Int'l. Airport: 9 miles/ 14 km, 25 minutes.

Worldwide Reservations
www.preferredhotels.com
800.323.7500 U.S.A./Canada
00.800.3237.5001 Europe (UIFN)
Other areas: See page 192

HOTEL GRAND PACIFIC

Classical style combined with European elegance and excellent service set the standard for a luxury experience that is heightened by the hotel's spectacular views. The landscaped forecourt includes water features and sculptural elements. Original and commissioned artworks complement the décor of both the guestrooms and the public spaces. Located downtown directly on Victoria's scenic Inner Harbour. Close to Legislative Buildings, Conference Centre and major shopping and business areas. Victoria Int'l. Airport: 25 miles/40 km, 40 minutes.

Worldwide Reservations

www.preferredhotels.com

800.323.7500 U.S.A./Canada

00.800.3237.5001 Europe (UIFN)

Other areas: See page 192

ACCOMMODATIONS: 304 total guestrooms, including 46 suites, each with balcony, duvets, newspaper, mini-bar, in-room safe, hair dryer, coffeemaker and video check-out. Ladies Executive Rooms available with additional amenities.

FACILITIES/SERVICES: Spa, full-service health club and pool, Marine Adventure Centre, concierge, in-room entertainment systems, complimentary parking and meeting rooms.

BUSINESS SERVICES: Complimentary in-room Internet access, fax, photocopying and secretarial services available.

DINING: "The Pacific Restaurant" offers an array of dishes with a Pacific Northwest flavor. "The Courtyard Café" offers espresso, cappuccino and light fare.

MEETINGS: Total Meeting Rooms: 12
Total Sq. Ft.: 12,000 / Sq. M.: 1,117

RATES: CAD 229.00 to 1,500.00; Corporate, Group, Package rates.

Mr. Stephen Webb
General Manager

463 Belleville Street
Victoria, British Columbia V8V 1X3, Canada
Tel: +1.250.386.0450
Fax: +1.250.380.4474
Email: reserve@hotelgrandpacific.com
www.hotelgrandpacific.com

METROPOLITAN HOTEL, TORONTO

A contemporary hotel in the heart of downtown Toronto, where guests will enjoy exceptional service, outstanding amenities, exquisite dining and remarkable pleasures. *A place for the connected to connect.* Downtown, adjacent to City Hall, within walking distance of the city's financial, commercial and cultural heart. Minutes from Eaton Centre, the Royal Ontario Museum, the Art Gallery of Ontario, SkyDome, premier theater and Toronto attractions. Pearson Int'l. Airport: 15 miles/25 km, 30 minutes.

ACCOMMODATIONS: 422 total guestrooms, including 58 suites, each with European linens and down duvets, broadband connectivity, two dual-line phones, computer/fax, data port, voice mail, fully stocked bar and opening windows.

FACILITIES/SERVICES: Les Clefs d'Or Concierge, fitness center, pool, whirlpool, massage, dry cleaning, turndown service and downtown limousine service.

BUSINESS SERVICES: On-site Business Center with state-of-the-art equipment, broadband connectivity, video conferencing and audio-visual services.

DINING: "Hemispheres Restaurant and Bistro" has redefined haute cuisine with the freshest, most exciting influences from around the world. Reflecting the exotic ingredients of the Pacific Rim, "Lai Wah Heen" serves the finest Cantonese cuisine in an elegant atmosphere.

MEETINGS: Total Meeting Rooms: 17
Total Sq. Ft.: 13,000 / Sq. M.: 1,210

RATES: CAD 280.00 to 420.00; Corporate, Group, Package rates.

Mr. Jeremy Roncoroni,
Hotel Manager

108 Chestnut Street
Toronto, Ontario M5G 1R3, Canada
Tel: +1.416.977.5000
Fax: +1.416.977.9513
Email: reservations@metropolitan.com
www.metropolitan.com

Worldwide Reservations
www.preferredhotels.com
800.323.7500 U.S.A./Canada
00.800.3237.5001 Europe (UIFN)
Other areas: See page 192

Opening March 2003

SOHO METROPOLITAN

The newest luxury hotel in Toronto opens in March 2003. The moment you set foot upon the marble floors of the Soho Met, you enter a world of exquisite delights and unparalleled convenience, where commitment to service and personal attention exceeds all expectations. The Soho Met is quite simply Toronto's finest. In the heart of Toronto's entertainment, theater and financial districts. Pearson Int'l. Airport: 10 miles/16 km, 25 minutes.

ACCOMMODATIONS: 88 total guestrooms, including 17 suites, and a three-story loft-style penthouse overlooking the city. All rooms feature soaker tubs, separate showers, heated marble bathroom floors, Frette linens, in-room office, mini-bars, smart technology, broadband connectivity and wireless Internet access and DVD players.

FACILITIES/SERVICES: Les Clefs d'Or Concierge, 10,000-square-foot spa, and state-of-the-art fitness center with steam room and lap pool.

BUSINESS SERVICES: On-site Business Center, state-of-the-art audio-visual equipment, broadband connectivity and wireless Internet access, limo service.

DINING: The "Senses Restaurant" mindset is leisure, the agenda, magnificent food and exceptional wine — for the sheer joy of it.

MEETINGS: Total Meeting Rooms: 2
Total Sq. Ft.: 2,230 / Sq. M.: 208

RATES: CAD 325.00 to 3,600.00; Corporate, Group, Package rates.

Mr. Scott Mawhinney,
General Manager

318 Wellington Street West
Toronto, Ontario M5V 3T4, Canada
Main Tel: +1.416.599.8800
Toll Free: +1.866.764.6638 (SOHOMET)
Fax: +1.416.599.8801
Email: soho@metropolitan.com
www.sohometropolitan.com

Worldwide Reservations
www.preferredhotels.com
800.323.7500 U.S.A./Canada
00.800.3237.5001 Europe (UIFN)
Other areas: See page 192

ROYAL CAPRI RESORT & SPA

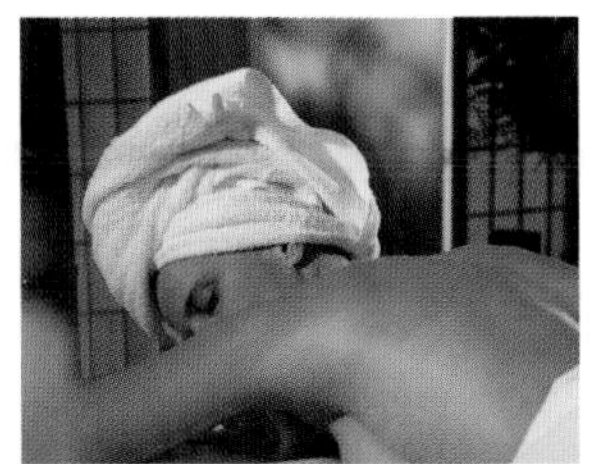

ACCOMMODATIONS: 288 total guestrooms, including 137 suites, each with two multi-line phones, data port, Internet access, voice mail, newspaper, safe, mini-bar, robes, hair dryer, DVD, terrace or balcony and full marble bathrooms with jetted tubs.

FACILITIES/SERVICES: Spa, fitness center, pool, outdoor Jacuzzi, land and water sports, fitness trail, championship golf nearby, library, billiards, salon and dry cleaning.

BUSINESS SERVICES: Business Center, secretarial services available. Translating services.

DINING: Four gourmet, à la carte restaurants offering Mediterranean, Pan-Asian, seafood and Continental cuisines. Beach Bar/Grill; beach/pool waiter service and room service available

MEETINGS: Total Meeting Rooms: 5 Total Sq. Ft.: 8,400 / Sq. M.: 780

RATES: USD 200.00 to 500.00 Per person/All inclusive. Corporate, Group, Package rates.

Mr. Kevin Wojciechowski, Executive Vice President

Carrettera Chetumal - Puerto Juarez
Km. 299, Playa del Carmen
Riviera Maya, c.p. 77711, Mexico
Tel: +52.984.801.4117
Fax: +52.984.804.4118
Email: kwojo@royalcapri.com
www.royalcapri.com

Expressing the generous soul of Mexico and commanding a pristine beachfront location between Playa del Carmen and Cancun, Royal Capri is a luxury oasis that embraces the elegance of traditional Mexican design and ensures unmatched standards of all inclusive service and pampering. Nestled in 71 tropical acres and surrounded by endless white beaches, the crystal clear Caribbean Sea and historic Mayan ruins. Cancun Int'l. Airport: 20 miles/33 km, 40 minutes.

Worldwide Reservations
www.preferredhotels.com
800.323.7500 U.S.A./Canada
00.800.3237.5001 Europe (UIFN)
Other areas: See page 192

THE WYNFREY HOTEL AT RIVERCHASE GALLERIA

From the sparkling French chandelier to the glistening Italian marble floors, this contemporary hotel was designed for luxury. Meticulously decorated with paintings and furnishings from the 1800s, the hotel is a Southern symbol of worldly elegance. The Wynfrey Hotel offers Southern hospitality and service with a world of charm. Attached to the spectacular Riverchase Galleria, which boasts 200 stores, 20 restaurants and 10 theaters. Birmingham Int'l. Airport: 20 miles/ 32 km, 25 minutes.

Worldwide Reservations

www.preferredhotels.com

800.323.7500 U.S.A./Canada

00.800.3237.5001 Europe (UIFN)

Other areas: See page 192

ACCOMMODATIONS: 329 total guestrooms, including 12 suites, each with data port, voice mail, Web TV, in-room games and movies, VCR available on request and hair dryer.

FACILITIES/SERVICES: Fitness center, concierge services, spa, seasonal outdoor pool and Jacuzzi, complimentary airport transportation, salon, dry cleaning and shoe shine. Hotel attached to Riverchase Galleria.

BUSINESS SERVICES: On-site Business Center and secretarial services available.

DINING: Choose "Winston's" for classic cuisine, "Chicory Grille" for informal dining or "Ivory's" for cocktails.

MEETINGS: Total Meeting Rooms: 21 Total Sq. Ft.: 30,000 / Sq. M.: 2,793

RATES: USD 155.00 to 1,200.00; Corporate, Group, Package rates.

Mr. Danny Hiatt, General Manager

1000 Riverchase Galleria
Birmingham, Alabama 35244, U.S.A.
Tel: +1.205.987.1600
Fax: +1.205.987.9552
Email: sales@wynfreyhotel.com
www.wynfrey.com

HOTEL CAPTAIN COOK

ACCOMMODATIONS: 547 total guestrooms, including 96 suites, each with multi-line phones, data port, voice mail, robes, hair dryer, down comforter duvet, 250-thread-count linens, oversized down pillows and Neutrogena bath products.

FACILITIES/SERVICES: Indoor pool, Jacuzzi, racquetball, massage, full-service separate athletic club, dry cleaning, salon, shops, concierge, turndown service and Austrian consulate.

BUSINESS SERVICES: On-site Business Center available.

DINING: The award-winning "Crows Nest" for fine dining, "Fletcher's" and the "Pantry" for casual fare, "Whale's Tail Coffee & Spirits" for gourmet coffee, cocktails and light fare.

MEETINGS: Total Meeting Rooms: 14
Total Sq. Ft.: 18,507 / Sq. M.: 1,723

RATES: USD 135.00 to 1,500.00; Corporate, Group, Package rates.

Mr. Walter J. Hickel, President

Warm teak and polished brass details echo the nautical heritage of the hotel's namesake. This landmark is set against the spectacular backdrop of the Alaskan wilderness. In the heart of the downtown business and shopping districts. Ted Stevens Anchorage Int'l. Airport: 6 miles/10 km, 15 minutes.

4th Avenue at K Street
Anchorage, Alaska 99501, U.S.A.
Tel: +1.907.276.6000
Fax: +1.907.343.2298
Email: info@captaincook.com
www.captaincook.com

Worldwide Reservations
www.preferredhotels.com
800.323.7500 U.S.A./Canada
00.800.3237.5001 Europe (UIFN)
Other areas: See page 192

THE PEABODY LITTLE ROCK

The Peabody Little Rock opened in February, 2002, following a $40-million renovation. Guests are welcomed into a truly inviting space, which is both dramatic and exquisitely comfortable. The lobby houses the famous Peabody Duck Fountain. Guestrooms are spacious and warm, and designed to please the most discerning of guests. Located in the heart of downtown Little Rock on the banks of the Arkansas River, the hotel is in the thriving River Market district, surrounded by historical and cultural attractions. Little Rock National Airport: 10 miles/16 km, 15 minutes.

Worldwide Reservations

www.preferredhotels.com

800.323.7500 U.S.A./Canada

00.800.3237.5001 Europe (UIFN)

Other areas: See page 192

ACCOMMODATIONS: 418 total guestrooms, including 22 suites, each with two multi-line phones, Internet access, data port, voice mail, hair dryer and iron and ironing board.

FACILITIES/SERVICES: Concierge services, fitness center, salon, dry cleaning and shops.

BUSINESS SERVICES: On-site Business Center.

DINING: "Capriccio" offers classic Northern Italian cuisine. "The Lobby Bar's" 42-foot granite bar is the social rendezvous. "Mallards," an intimate bar with a club-like atmosphere, has three separate seating areas. 24-hour in-room dining also available.

MEETINGS: Total Meeting Rooms: 14 Total Sq. Ft.: 40,000 / Sq. M.: 3,724

RATES: USD 189.00 to 1,500.00; Corporate, Group, Package rates.

Mr. Timothy S. Gonser, Vice President & General Manager

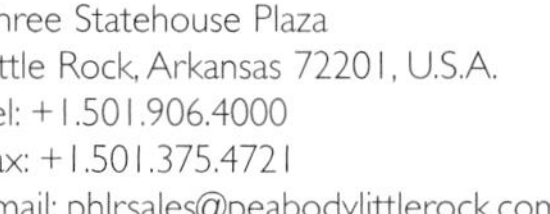

Three Statehouse Plaza
Little Rock, Arkansas 72201, U.S.A.
Tel: +1.501.906.4000
Fax: +1.501.375.4721
Email: phlrsales@peabodylittlerock.com
www.peabodylittlerock.com

QUAIL LODGE RESORT & GOLF CLUB

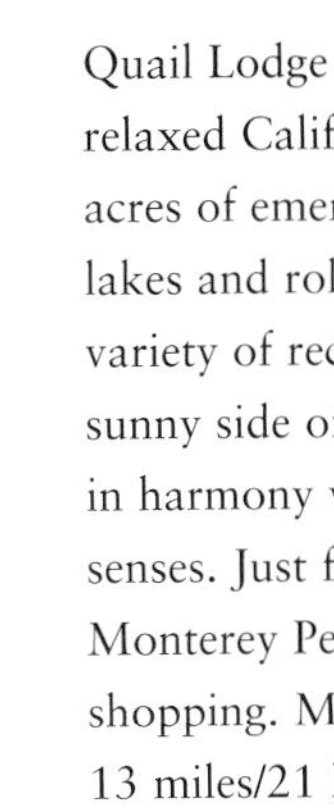

Quail Lodge conveys a casual elegance with relaxed California style. Nestled among 850 acres of emerald green fairways, sparkling lakes and rolling hills, this resort offers a variety of recreational activities. On the sunny side of Carmel, this haven of serenity in harmony with nature awakens all the senses. Just five minutes from Carmel, on the Monterey Peninsula. Close to beaches and shopping. Monterey Peninsula Airport: 13 miles/21 km, 20 minutes.

ACCOMMODATIONS: 97 total guestrooms, including 16 suites, each with multi-line phones, data port, voice mail, Internet access, newspaper, mini-bar, robes, hair dryer. VCR available on request.

FACILITIES/SERVICES: Championship golf, hiking and jogging trails, spa, fitness room, tennis, child care services, dry cleaning, shoe shine and shops.

BUSINESS SERVICES: On-site Business Center, secretarial and translating services on request.

DINING: "The Covey" offers inventive, contemporary cuisine. Enjoy attentive tableside service overlooking the rolling hills of Carmel. Enjoy panoramic views of lush fairways while enjoying breakfast and lunch in the casual atmosphere of the "Club Dining Room." Light snacks and beverages are served on "The Covey Deck" overlooking Mallard Lake.

MEETINGS: Total Meeting Rooms: 7
Total Sq. Ft.: 8,301 / Sq. M.: 773

RATES: USD 265.00 to 900.00; Corporate, Group, Package rates.

Mr. Bruce Pofahl, Resort Manager

8205 Valley Greens Drive
Carmel, California 93923, U.S.A.
Tel: +1.831.624.2888
Fax: +1.831.624.3726
Email: info@quaillodge.com
www.quaillodge.com

Worldwide Reservations
www.preferredhotels.com
800.323.7500 U.S.A./Canada
00.800.3237.5001 Europe (UIFN)
Other areas: See page 192

SURF & SAND RESORT

This intimate, Mediterranean-style paradise offers informal luxury with a soft pastel scheme, travertine marble baths, plantation shutters and spectacular ocean views. Rolling surf and Pacific sunsets set the stage for relaxation and romance. Situated along 500 feet (152 meters) of white sand beach midway between Los Angeles and San Diego, directly on Laguna Beach. John Wayne Orange County Airport: 12 miles/19 km, 20 minutes.

ACCOMMODATIONS: 165 total guestrooms, including 13 suites, each with two phones, data port, voice mail, newspaper, CD player, safe, mini-bar and robes.

FACILITIES/SERVICES: Spa, fitness center, concierge, child care services, dry cleaning and shops.

BUSINESS SERVICES: On-site Business Center and secretarial services available.

DINING: "Splashes" serves a Mediterranean-inspired menu. Guests can enjoy indoor or patio dining with spectacular sunset views.

MEETINGS: Total Meeting Rooms: 13 Total Sq. Ft.: 10,000 / Sq. M.: 931

RATES: USD 295.00 to 1,100.00; Corporate, Group, Package rates.

Mr. Blaise Bartell, General Manager

1555 South Coast Highway
Laguna Beach, California 92651, U.S.A.
Tel: +1.949.497.4477
Fax: +1.949.494.7653
Email: surfandsandresort@jcresorts.com
www.jcresorts.com

Worldwide Reservations

www.preferredhotels.com
800.323.7500 U.S.A./Canada
00.800.3237.5001 Europe (UIFN)
Other areas: See page 192

Opening Spring 2003

THE BALBOA BAY CLUB RESORT & SPA

ACCOMMODATIONS: 131 total guestrooms, including 8 suites, each with multi-line phones, data port, high-speed Internet access, voice mail, safe, robes and hair dryer.

FACILITIES/SERVICES: Spa, Olympic pool, concierge services, shoe shine, fitness center, child care services, salon, dry cleaning and shops. Yachting, sailing and boating are also offered.

BUSINESS SERVICES: Business services available.

DINING: "First Cabin" features award-winning international cuisine, and "Duke's Place" is the resort's entertainment lounge.

MEETINGS: Total Meeting Rooms: 10
Total Sq. Ft.: 15,464 / Sq. M.: 1,440

RATES: USD 225.00 to 3,000.00; Corporate, Group, Package rates.

Mr. Henry Schielein,
President and C.O.O.

  @

1221 W. Coast Highway
Newport Beach, California 92663,
U.S.A.
Tel: +1.949.645.5000
Fax: +1.949.630.4215
Email: mail@balboabayclub.com
www.balboabayclub.com

The redeveloped resort built in Italian Mediterranean style, with classical columns, domes, delicate arches and plantation-style furniture, reflects the casual elegance of Newport Beach. The only waterfront resort in Newport Beach, the hotel is situated on 15 bayfront acres and commands a spectacular view. Relax and rejuvenate in the charm of the California Riviera. Centrally located near Newport Beach's Fashion Island and Balboa Peninsula. John Wayne Airport: 8 miles/13 km, 15 minutes.

Worldwide Reservations
www.preferredhotels.com
800.323.7500 U.S.A./Canada
00.800.3237.5001 Europe (UIFN)
Other areas: See page 192

MIRAMONTE RESORT, INDIAN WELLS

Miramonte is an intimate Tuscan-style retreat with curved archways and impressive stonework. Nestled in the foothills of the Santa Rosa Mountains on 11 acres (5 hectares) of lushly landscaped gardens, this intimate oasis offers attentive service while immersing guests in an inviting and tranquil old-world atmosphere. Located in the heart of Indian Wells, only minutes from the boutiques, restaurants and galleries of El Paseo. Palm Springs Airport: 10 miles/16 km, 20 minutes.

ACCOMMODATIONS: 222 total guestrooms, including 5 suites, each with three phones, data port, voice mail, newspaper, safe, mini-bar, robes and VCR on request.

FACILITIES/SERVICES: Spa, fitness center, concierge, child care services, dry cleaning, shoe shine, salon and gift shop.

BUSINESS SERVICES: Business Center open seven days per week.

DINING: "Brissago" offers unique Northern Italian cuisine in an elegant bistro setting and features a strolling classical guitarist nightly.

MEETINGS: Total Meeting Rooms: 13 Total Sq. Ft.: 14,000 / Sq. M.: 1,303

RATES: USD 129.00 to 1,500.00; Corporate, Group, Package rates.

Ms. Danna Holck, General Manager

45000 Indian Wells Lane
Palm Springs/Indian Wells, California 92210, U.S.A.
Tel: +1.760.341.2200
Fax: +1.760.568.0541
Email: miramonte.info@miramonte resort.com
www.miramonte-resort.com

Worldwide Reservations
www.preferredhotels.com
800.323.7500 U.S.A./Canada
00.800.3237.5001 Europe (UIFN)
Other areas: See page 192

RANCHO BERNARDO INN

ACCOMMODATIONS: 287 total guestrooms, including 13 suites, each with data port, voice mail, safe, mini-bar, hair dryer and VCR on request.

FACILITIES/SERVICES: 18-hole championship and 27-hole executive golf courses and pro shops, tennis courts, pools, fitness center, spa, bike rental, concierge, dry cleaning and extensive Children's Programs.

BUSINESS SERVICES: On-site Business Center and secretarial services available.

DINING: Offering upscale French cuisine in the top-rated "El Bizcocho" dining room, and California cuisine in the "Veranda Grill."

MEETINGS: Total Meeting Rooms: 15 Total Sq. Ft.: 15,000 / Sq. M.: 1,396

RATES: USD 259.00 to 1,000.00; Corporate, Group, Package rates.

Mr. Bob Peckenpaugh,
Hotel Manager

17550 Bernardo Oaks Drive
San Diego, California 92128, U.S.A.
Tel: +1.858.675.8500
Fax: +1.858.675.8501
Email:
ranchobernardoinn@jcresorts.com
www.jcresorts.com

A sophisticated California Mission-style resort, featuring golf, tennis and a full-service spa. Reminiscent of a country estate with lush California landscaping, and set against the backdrop of the San Pasquel Mountains, the Inn has a gracious and unpretentious style with genuine warmth, affording guests total relaxation. Located in San Diego North, with access to a full range of attractions. San Diego Int'l. Airport: 28 miles/45 km, 30 minutes.

Worldwide Reservations

www.preferredhotels.com
800.323.7500 U.S.A./Canada
00.800.3237.5001 Europe (UIFN)
Other areas: See page 192

LA VALENCIA HOTEL

Intimate and charming, La Valencia Hotel has been the place to stay in La Jolla since opening in 1926. Just steps from the Pacific, it is fondly known as "the Jewel of La Jolla." On the Pacific Ocean in picturesque La Jolla. San Diego Int'l. Airport: 12 miles/19 km, 20 minutes.

ACCOMMODATIONS: 116 total guestrooms, including 17 suites, each with two multi-line phones, data port, voice mail, VCR, safe, mini-bar, robes, hair dryer, iron and ironing board and newspaper.

FACILITIES/SERVICES: Pool, whirlpool, fitness center, spa services, concierge, dry cleaning and shoe shine.

BUSINESS SERVICES: Business, secretarial and translating services on request.

DINING: "The Sky Room" offers elegant California cuisine, "Whaling Bar & Grill" offers tableside service in a pub-like atmosphere and "Mediterranean Room" offers casual dining both indoors and on the Ocean View Terrace.

MEETINGS: Total Meeting Rooms: 3
Total Sq. Ft.: 5,000 / Sq. M.: 466

RATES: USD 300.00 to 3,500.00

Mr. Michael J. Ullman,
General Manager

1132 Prospect Street
La Jolla, California 92037, U.S.A.
Tel: +1.858.454.0771
Fax: +1.858.456.3921
Email: info@lavalencia.com
www.lavalencia.com

Worldwide Reservations

www.preferredhotels.com
800.323.7500 U.S.A./Canada
00.800.3237.5001 Europe (UIFN)
Other areas: See page 192

THE HUNTINGTON HOTEL & NOB HILL SPA

ACCOMMODATIONS: 135 total guestrooms, including 35 suites, each with mini-bar, safe, multi-line phones, data port, voice mail, fax machine and complimentary DSL access. VCR available on request.

FACILITIES/SERVICES: The Nob Hill Spa and Wellness Center, overlooking the glorious San Francisco skyline, includes an indoor pool, a Jacuzzi, saunas and steam rooms, couple's massage room, Vichy shower and soaking bathtub, massage, facial, nail, and body treatments. Complimentary tea or sherry service, chauffeured sedan, dry cleaning, child care services, shoe shine, concierge services and health club.

BUSINESS SERVICES: New on-site, full-service Business Center.

DINING: The "Big 4 Restaurant" for fine dining features contemporary American cuisine.

MEETINGS: Total Meeting Rooms: 4
Total Sq. Ft.: 1,800 / Sq. M.: 168

RATES: USD 290.00 to 1,100.00; Corporate, Group, Package rates.

Ms. Gail R. Isono, General Manager

1075 California Street
San Francisco, California 94108, U.S.A.
Tel: +1.415.474.5400
Fax: +1.415.474.6227
Email:
reservations@huntingtonhotel.com
www.huntingtonhotel.com

The famed cable cars stop at the front doors of this elegant and intimate landmark, perched atop prestigious Nob Hill. Located off the lobby is the one-of-a-kind Nob Hill Spa, which combines the Japanese, Chinese, Italian and Victorian influences found in the architecture and people of San Francisco. At California and Taylor streets, four blocks from Union Square and the Theater District. San Francisco Int'l. Airport: 15 miles/24 km, 30 minutes.

Worldwide Reservations
www.preferredhotels.com
800.323.7500 U.S.A./Canada
00.800.3237.5001 Europe (UIFN)
Other areas: See page 192

Opening Winter 2003

HOTEL VALENCIA SANTANA ROW

Opening in January 2003, this new hotel evokes the feeling of a grand Tuscan palazzo that has weathered the ages. An expansive open-air courtyard and rooftop wine terrace open-pit fire and water features along with breathtaking sunset views over the Santa Cruz Mountains. Located three miles west of downtown San Jose in the heart of Santana Row, with shopping, dining, cinemas and residences. San Jose Int'l. Airport is a 10-minute drive and San Francisco Int'l. Airport is a 40-minute drive.

ACCOMMODATIONS: 213 total guestrooms, including 16 suites, each with custom made bed; "Lather" bath amenities, bathrobes and mini bar; high-speed Internet access at desk and bedside; two dual-line speakerphones, one cordless; voice, data and video network infrastructure available.

FACILITIES/SERVICES: Outdoor heated pool with sun deck overlooking Santana Row, whirlpool, fitness center, spa, concierge, laundry and valet, shoe shine and children's program.

BUSINESS SERVICES: Full-service business center providing wireless Internet access.

DINING: "Citrus" features a fresh regional menu all day, "V Bar" flows into open-air courtyard and overlooks Santana Row. "Cielo" Wine Terrace features grotto water feature and fireplace.

MEETINGS: Total Meeting Rooms: 5
Total Sq. Ft.: 3,804 / Sq. M.: 354

RATES: USD 125.00 to 385.00; Corporate, Group, Package rates.

Mr. Martin Duane, General Manager

355 Santana Row
San Jose, California 98128, U.S.A.
Tel: +1.408.551.0010
Fax: +1.408.551.0550
Email: santanarow@valenciagroup.com
www.hotelvalencia.com

Worldwide Reservations
www.preferredhotels.com
800.323.7500 U.S.A./Canada
00.800.3237.5001 Europe (UIFN)
Other areas: See page 192

BACARA RESORT & SPA

ACCOMMODATIONS: 311 total guestrooms and 49 suites, each with balcony or patio; many with fireplaces and ocean views. All rooms include three multi-line phones, data port, personalized voice mail, DVD player, high-speed Internet access, CD player and robes.

FACILITIES/SERVICES: 42,000 square-foot (3,910 square-meter) spa with 36 treatment rooms, fitness center and full-service salon. Golf, hiking and biking. Ranch at Bacara, 1,000 acre working lemon-avocado ranch, available for driving schools and other themed events. Executive Conference Center, Business Center, Ballroom and 211-seat Screening Room.

DINING: "Miro," for upscale, fine dining; "The Bistro," for casual dining and "Spa Café," serving local, organic cuisine.

MEETINGS: Total Meeting Rooms: 18
Indoor Sq. Ft.: 25,000 / Sq. M.: 2,323
Outdoor Sq. Ft.: 10,000 / Sq. M.: 929

RATES: USD 395.00 to 5,000.00; Corporate, Group, Package rates.

8301 Hollister Avenue
Santa Barbara, California 93117, U.S.A.
Tel: +1.805.968.0100
Toll Free: +1.877.422.4245
Fax: +1.805.968.1800
Email: info@bacararesort.com
www.bacararesort.com

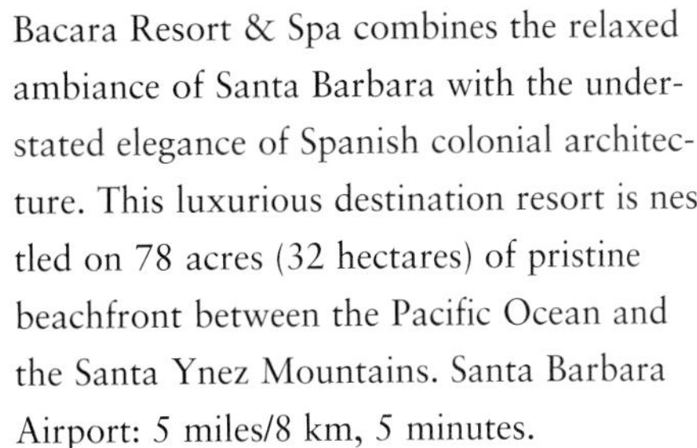

Bacara Resort & Spa combines the relaxed ambiance of Santa Barbara with the understated elegance of Spanish colonial architecture. This luxurious destination resort is nestled on 78 acres (32 hectares) of pristine beachfront between the Pacific Ocean and the Santa Ynez Mountains. Santa Barbara Airport: 5 miles/8 km, 5 minutes.

Worldwide Reservations
www.preferredhotels.com
800.323.7500 U.S.A./Canada
00.800.3237.5001 Europe (UIFN)
Other areas: See page 192

VINEYARD CREEK HOTEL, SPA AND CONFERENCE CENTER

Opening June 2002. The Vineyard Creek Hotel is a Mediterranean building centered around two large courtyards. The grounds are lushly landscaped, creating a secluded oasis within the city. The rooms are elegant and classic in design. In the heart of California's famed wine country and a short walk to Railroad Square, which features a collection of antique shops, gift shops and restaurants. The hotel adjoins Santa Rosa Creek, with its landscaped walking and bike trails. San Francisco Int'l. Airport: 55 miles/88 km, 90 minutes.

ACCOMMODATIONS: 155 total guestrooms, including 20 suites, each with T-1 high-speed Internet access, multi-line cordless phones, voice mail, refreshment center, safe, down comforters, aromatherapy, newspapers, robes, slippers, fresh flowers, turndown tea service and in-room French press coffee service.

FACILITIES/SERVICES: Fully equipped spa with health and fitness center, outdoor pool and 24-hour concierge.

BUSINESS SERVICES: Secretarial services available.

DINING: "Brasserie de La Mer," Sonoma County's finest French seafood cuisine restaurant, offers the best of local fare and serves California's finest wines from nearby wineries.

MEETINGS: Total Meeting Rooms: 15 Total Sq. Ft.: 21,000 / Sq. M.: 1,955

RATES: USD 210.00 to 400.00; Corporate, Group, Package rates.

Mr. Dan Evans, General Manager

170 Railroad Road
Santa Rosa, California 95401, U.S.A.
Tel: +1.707.636.7100
Fax: +1.707.636.7277
Email: info@vineyardcreek.com
www.vineyardcreek.com

Worldwide Reservations
www.preferredhotels.com
800.323.7500 U.S.A./Canada
00.800.3237.5001 Europe (UIFN)
Other areas: See page 192

THE PINES LODGE

Natural rustic pine, heavy tapestries and fresh mountain wild flowers complement this intimate lodge nestled among groves of aspen and pine trees with magnificent views. Relax after a full day of skiing or 18 holes of golf in this tranquil setting. Woven into the majestic setting of Beaver Creek, Colorado. Denver Int'l. Airport: 110 miles/177 km, 2 hours. Eagle County Airport: 30 miles/48 km, 20 minutes.

ACCOMMODATIONS: 72 total guestrooms, including 12 suites, each with two phones, data port, voice mail, VCR, robes, refrigerator and coffeemaker.

FACILITIES/SERVICES: Snow skiing, year-round ice skating, horseback riding, hot air ballooning, snow-mobiling, fishing, golf, river rafting, hiking, fitness center, tennis, child care services, dry cleaning and concierge.

BUSINESS SERVICES: High-speed Internet terminals in all guest rooms. Personalized secretarial and guest services.

DINING: The Pines Lodge's "Grouse Mountain Grill" features creative top-rated Regional American cuisine.

MEETINGS: Total Meeting Rooms: 6
Total Sq. Ft.: 3,145 / Sq. M.: 293

RATES: USD 99.00 to 2,970.00; Corporate, Group, Package rates.

Mr. Steven Rose, General Manager

141 Scott Hill Road
Beaver Creek, Colorado 81620, U.S.A.
Tel: +1.970.845.7900
Fax: +1.970.845.7809
Email: vbcrp@vailresorts.com
www.vbcrp.com

Worldwide Reservations
www.preferredhotels.com
800.323.7500 U.S.A./Canada
00.800.3237.5001 Europe (UIFN)
Other areas: See page 192

CONCIERGE

THE BROADMOOR

ACCOMMODATIONS: 700 total guestrooms, including 107 suites, each with two multi-line phones, data port, voice mail, newspaper, safe, mini-bar, robes and CD players.

FACILITIES/SERVICES: World-renowned spa, three golf courses, fitness center, tennis, child care services, dry cleaning, shoe shine, salon, florist, concierge and shops.

BUSINESS SERVICES: On-site Business Center, secretarial and translating services available.

DINING: With 10 different restaurants and lounges featuring a variety of delectable cuisines, The Broadmoor can satisfy every dining preference and palate.

MEETINGS: Total Meeting Rooms: 52
Total Sq. Ft.: 110,000 / Sq. M.: 10,241

RATES: USD 230.00 to 2,500.00; Corporate, Group, Package rates.

Ms. Ann Alba, Resident Manager

One Lake Avenue
Colorado Springs, Colorado 80906, U.S.A.
Tel: +1.719.634.7711
Fax: +1.719.577.5700
Email: sales@broadmoor.com
www.broadmoor.com

Recently renovated, this "Grand Dame of the Rockies" continues to shine brightly as one of the world's premier resorts. On 3,000 acres (1,214 hectares) at the foot of the Colorado Rockies, this invigorating and luxurious mountain retreat offers a legacy of elegance, impeccable service and exquisite cuisine. Minutes from downtown Colorado Springs, Pikes Peak Cog Railway, Garden of the Gods and Cheyenne Mountain Zoo. Colorado Springs Airport: 12 miles/19 km, 20 minutes.

Worldwide Reservations
www.preferredhotels.com
800.323.7500 U.S.A./Canada
00.800.3237.5001 Europe (UIFN)
Other areas: See page 192

THE BROWN PALACE HOTEL

For more than a century, the Italian Renaissance style of this historic landmark has delighted guests with its onyx walls, terrazzo floors and gold leaf highlights. Once inside and away from the bustle of the city, guests can relax while enjoying afternoon tea in the luxurious atrium lobby, complete with soothing sounds of a harp or piano. Located in the heart of downtown, an easy walk to Denver's museums, performing arts venues and major league sporting events. Denver Int'l. Airport: 25 miles/40 km, 40 minutes.

ACCOMMODATIONS: 230 total guestrooms, including 25 suites, each with two multi-line phones, data port, newspaper, robes, complimentary high-speed Internet access and private voice mail.

FACILITIES/SERVICES: Fitness center, full-service concierge, dry cleaning, salon, business center and florist.

BUSINESS SERVICES: On-site Business Center, secretarial and translating services available.

DINING: Choice of three restaurants: Enjoy fine dining in "Palace Arms;" breakfast, lunch or Dom Perignon Sunday brunch in "Ellyngton's;" casual dining with piano bar in local favorite "Ship Tavern;" spirits and cigars in "Churchill Bar."

MEETINGS: Total Meeting Rooms: 14
Total Sq. Ft.: 15,000 / Sq. M.: 1,396

RATES: USD 235.00 to 925.00; Corporate, Group, Package rates.

Mr. Armel Santens,
Managing Director

321 Seventeenth Street
Denver, Colorado 80202, U.S.A.
Tel: +1.303.297.3111
Fax: +1.303.312.5900
Email: marketing@brownpalace.com
www.brownpalace.com

Worldwide Reservations
www.preferredhotels.com
800.323.7500 U.S.A./Canada
00.800.3237.5001 Europe (UIFN)
Other areas: See page 192

CITY SIGHTS, CITY NIGHTS — BOOK YOUR NEXT WEEKEND GETAWAY AT PREFERRED

FROM BOSTON'S BEACON HILL TO London's new Notting Hill, Preferred's urban hotels make an ideal venue for a weekend getaway. Experience the energy and excitement of the world's great cities. Catch a show, shop, take in an exhibit at a world-class museum, dine on sumptuous cuisine — all while enjoying the outstanding amenities and service for which Preferred hotels are renowned. Have business in Boston? **Fifteen Beacon,** located across from the Boston Common, puts you within minutes of the State House, financial district and the fashionable shops on exclusive Newbury Street — and features Boston's most extensive wine cellar. Enjoy innovative cuisine at LaCroix at **The Rittenhouse,** an intimate oasis on Philadelphia's Rittenhouse Square. Theater lovers, book a weekend at **The Landmark London.** Located in fashionable Marylebone, the new Notting Hill, The Landmark sits with the famous West End — London's theater district — on its doorstep. Or explore the rich architecture and history of Prague, where the **Hotel Palace Praha,** built in 1906 in Art Nouveau style, is centrally located adjacent to the famous Wenceslav's Square. When you've had your fill of the hectic urban pace, treat yourself to a massage, or have a nightcap in your room while looking out over the lights of the city.

For more information on a Preferred getaway, refer to page 192 for a local reservation number or visit our Web site at www.preferredhotels.com.

KEYSTONE LODGE

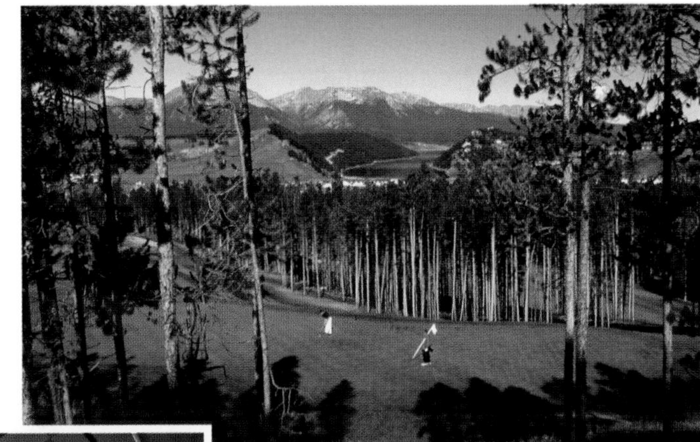

Lakeside, in a charming alpine-style village, Keystone Lodge offers guests a myriad of activities and gracious service. Faithful to Laurance Rockefeller's original vision, this hotel both reflects and enhances its spectacular setting. Surrounded by the Rockies and thousands of acres of National Forest, Keystone Lodge is located in the heart of Keystone Resort, a premier year-round destination. Denver Int'l. Airport: 90 miles/ 120 km, 90 minutes.

ACCOMMODATIONS: 152 total guestrooms, including 14 suites, each with two multi-line phones, data port, voice mail, newspaper, iron and ironing board, hair dryer and robes. VCR and fax available on request.

FACILITIES/SERVICES: World-class skiing, ice skating, snowmobiling, snowshoeing, cross country skiing and sleigh rides in winter; 36 holes of championship golf, horseback riding, mountain biking, rafting, hiking, fly-fishing and tennis in summer.

BUSINESS SERVICES: Adjacent to the Keystone Convention Center, the largest meeting facility in the Rocky Mountains. Business Center, A/V services and satellite teleconferencing.

DINING: Keystone Resort offers more than 30 dining options, including two AAA Four Diamond™-rated restaurants, "The Keystone Ranch" and "Alpenglow Stube."

MEETINGS: Total Meeting Rooms: 50
Total Sq. Ft.: 100,000 / Sq. M.: 9,310

RATES: USD 89.00 to 285.00; Group, Package rates.

Mr. John Luckett, General Manager

22010 U.S. Highway 6
Keystone, Colorado 80435, U.S.A.
Tel: +1.888.697.0060
Fax: +1.303.756.8844
Email: keystoneinfo@vailresorts.com
www.keystoneresort.com

Worldwide Reservations

www.preferredhotels.com
800.323.7500 U.S.A./Canada
00.800.3237.5001 Europe (UIFN)
Other areas: See page 192

THE LODGE AT VAIL

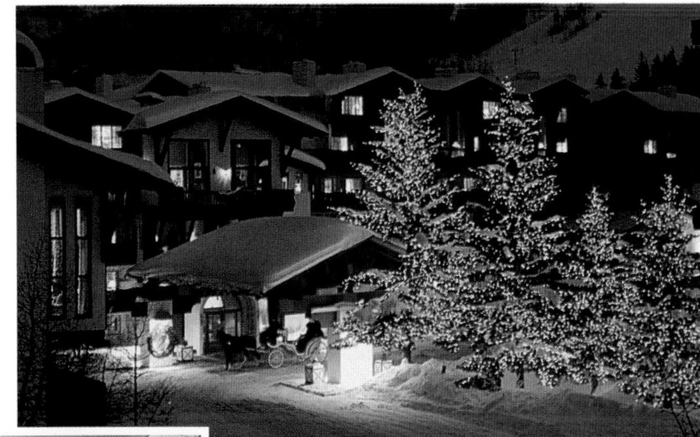

ACCOMMODATIONS: 165 total guestrooms, including 49 suites, each with dual-line phone, data port, voice mail, VCR, newspaper and robes.

FACILITIES/SERVICES: Alpine and cross-country skiing, golf, whitewater rafting, kayaking, fly-fishing, hot air ballooning, hiking, biking, fitness center, child care services, dry cleaning, concierge and shops.

BUSINESS SERVICES: On-site business services. Secretarial and translating services available.

DINING: Signature dining in the "Wildflower," Vail's only Mobil four-star award recipient, offers creative American cuisine; and "Cucina Rustica" features skier's buffets and Italian-inspired fare. "Mickey's Piano Bar" is a Vail tradition.

MEETINGS: Total Meeting Rooms: 7 Total Sq. Ft.: 9,269 / Sq. M.: 863

RATES: USD 120.00 to 5,300.00; Corporate, Group, Package rates.

Mr. Wolfgang Triebnig,
General Manager

174 East Gore Creek Drive
Vail, Colorado 81657, U.S.A.
Tel: +1.970.476.5011
Fax: +1.970.476.7425
Email: reservations@lodgeatvail.com
www.lodgeatvail.com

This charming European-style hotel combines the rustic nature of Colorado with the elegance and charm of an old world inn. The Lodge is located in the heart of Vail Village, just steps from world-class skiing, shopping and dining. Guests will enjoy relaxed luxury with the warmth of Western hospitality in the perfect mountain location. Denver Int'l. Airport: 120 miles/193 km, 120 minutes. Vail/Eagle County Airport: 35 miles/56 km, 40 minutes.

Worldwide Reservations
www.preferredhotels.com
800.323.7500 U.S.A./Canada
00.800.3237.5001 Europe (UIFN)
Other areas: See page 192

HOTEL GEORGE

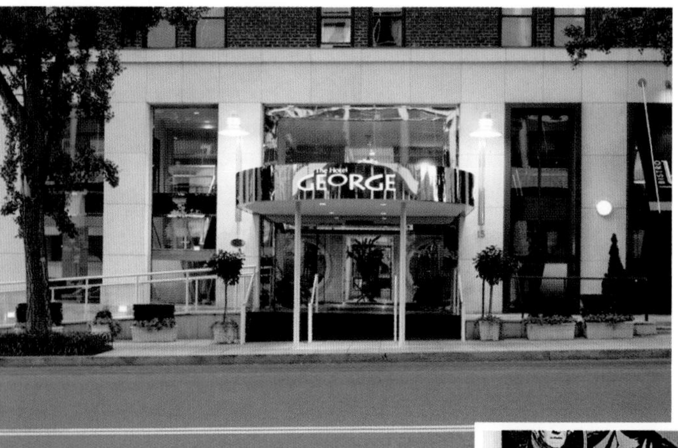

Providing guests with an intimate and contemporary setting and located at the nucleus of the Washington government, culture and business district, the George achieves a perfect balance between personalized service and a sophisticated hotel experience. Situated just west of North Capitol Street, one block from the Union Station Metro stop and walking distance to the U.S. Capitol, Smithsonian Institution and Supreme Court. Reagan Nat'l. Airport: 4 miles/6 km. Dulles Int'l. Airport: 25 miles/38 km.

Worldwide Reservations
www.preferredhotels.com
800.323.7500 U.S.A./Canada
00.800.3237.5001 Europe (UIFN)
Other areas: See page 192

ACCOMMODATIONS: 139 total guestrooms, including 3 suites, each immaculate guest room features 300 thread-count linens, multi-line cordless phones, data port, voice mail, newspaper, safe, mini-bar, CD/stereo clock radio with nature sounds, iron and ironing board, umbrella and robes, high-speed Internet access; some rooms equipped with fax machines.

FACILITIES/SERVICES: Complimentary fitness center, steam room, concierge services, child care services, dry cleaning, shoe shine and billiards room.

BUSINESS SERVICES: Secretarial services. All meeting rooms equipped with high-speed Internet access.

DINING: Dine in the George's award-winning restaurant "Bistro Bis." Chef Jeffrey Buben's celebrated menu features creative interpretations of classic French bistro fare.

MEETINGS: Total Meeting Rooms: 4 Total Sq. Ft.: 2,488 / Sq. M.: 232

RATES: USD 250.00 to 900.00; Corporate, Group, Package rates.

Ms. Dixie Eng, General Manager

15 E Street, NW
Washington, D.C. 20001, U.S.A.
Tel: +1.202.347.4200
Fax: +1.202.347.4213
Email: rooms@hotelgeorge.com
www.hotelgeorge.com

WASHINGTON TERRACE HOTEL

ACCOMMODATIONS: 220 total guestrooms, including 39 suites, each with cordless phone, data port, high-speed Internet access, radio/CD player, mini-bar, coffee maker and in-room safe that holds laptop. Corporate level floors.

FACILITIES/SERVICES: Fitness center, laundry and dry cleaning.

BUSINESS SERVICES: On-site Business Center with concierge.

DINING: "15 ria," a bistro-style restaurant with a retro-style bar, features fresh local and regional products prepared in a straightforward fashion. Seasonal outdoor dining. Weekend brunch available.

MEETINGS: Total Meeting Rooms: 9 Total Sq. Ft.: 6,700 / Sq. M.: 624

RATES: USD 139.00 to 750.00; Corporate, Group, Package rates.

Mr. Peter Carroll, General Manager

1515 Rhode Island Avenue, NW
Washington, D.C. 20005, U.S.A.
Tel: +1.202.232.7000
Fax: +1.202.332.8436
Email: reservations@washingtonterracehotel.com
www.washingtonterracehotel.com

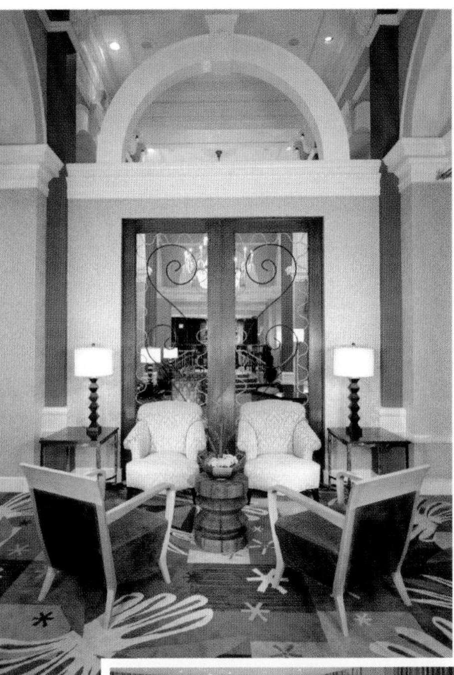

Highlighted by three beautifully landscaped terraces, The Washington Terrace is a serene oasis in the heart of a vibrant city. Guests will enjoy a sophisticated blend of boutique style and traditional touches as well as exceptional hospitality. Near Scott Circle in northwest Washington, six blocks from the White House. Three blocks from the Connecticut Avenue and K Street business and shopping districts. Near museums, monuments and National Zoo. Three blocks from Metro stations at Dupont Circle and McPherson Square. Reagan National Airport: 3 miles/ 4.8 km, 10 minutes.

Worldwide Reservations
www.preferredhotels.com
800.323.7500 U.S.A./Canada
00.800.3237.5001 Europe (UIFN)
Other areas: See page 192

HOTEL DU PONT

Long known for its Old World elegance, this 12-story Italian Renaissance hotel houses many original paintings, including three generations of Wyeths. Breathtaking scenery and a wealth of historical attractions are a short drive from the hotel's door. In downtown Wilmington, close to the historic Winterthur Museum and Gardens. Philadelphia Int'l. Airport: 19 miles/31 km, 25 minutes.

ACCOMMODATIONS: 217 total guestrooms, including 12 suites, each with voice mail in three languages, data port, newspaper, mini-bars, robes, TV entertainment center and in-room safe.

FACILITIES/SERVICES: 1,200-seat theater, fitness club with sauna, gift shop, shoe shine, hair salon, 24-hour room service and concierge.

BUSINESS SERVICES: On-site Business Center available.

DINING: Choice of two distinguished restaurants, the "Green Room" for French cuisine and "Brandywine Room" for American fare. Afternoon tea and cocktails are served in the Lobby Lounge.

MEETINGS: Total Meeting Rooms: 32 Total Sq. Ft.: 30,000 / Sq. M.: 2,793

RATES: USD 159.00 to 650.00; Corporate, Group, Package rates.

Ms. Deborah W. Hopkins, Director
DuPont Hospitality

11th and Market Streets
Wilmington, Delaware 19801, U.S.A.
Tel: +1.302.594.3100
Fax: +1.302.594.3108
Email: hotel.dupont@usa.dupont.com
www.hoteldupont.com

Worldwide Reservations

www.preferredhotels.com
800.323.7500 U.S.A./Canada
00.800.3237.5001 Europe (UIFN)
Other areas: See page 192

AMELIA ISLAND PLANTATION INN

ACCOMMODATIONS: 249 total guestrooms, including 3 suites, each oceanfront room features two multi-line phones, data port, voice mail, newspaper, safe, mini-bar, robes, hair dryer, video games, movies, in-room coffeemaker with premium coffee, 318-thread-count Egyptian linens and spa amenities.

FACILITIES/SERVICES: 3.5 miles of beach, 54 holes of championship golf, spa and salon, concierge, shoe shine, Health and Fitness Center, 23 clay tennis courts, dry cleaning, shopping, youth programs, child care services, nature tours and fishing.

BUSINESS SERVICES: Full-service Business Center, wireless Internet access.

DINING: Seven restaurants offer a variety of options from fine dining with contemporary regional cuisine to charmingly casual with the freshest seafood.

MEETINGS: Total Meeting Rooms: 25 Total Sq. Ft.: 49,000 / Sq. M.: 4,562

RATES: USD 175.00 to 352.00; Group, Package rates.

Mr. Walther Vliegen, Vice President & General Manager

6800 First Coast Highway
Amelia Island, Florida 32034, U.S.A.
Tel: +1.904.261.6161
Fax: +1.904.277.5159
Email: reservations@aipfl.com
www.aipfl.com

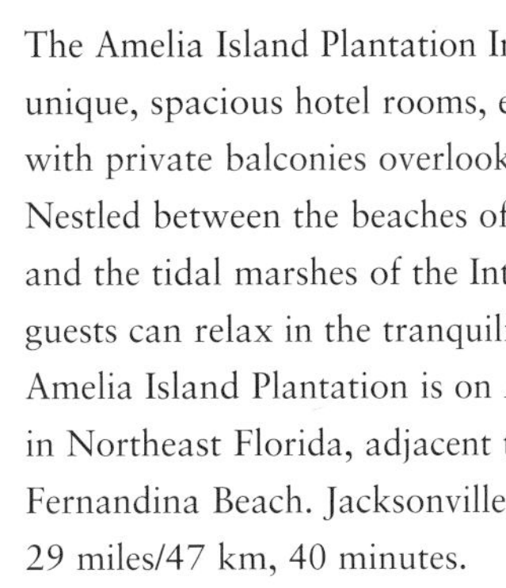

The Amelia Island Plantation Inn offers unique, spacious hotel rooms, each equipped with private balconies overlooking the ocean. Nestled between the beaches of the Atlantic and the tidal marshes of the Intracoastal, guests can relax in the tranquility of nature. Amelia Island Plantation is on Amelia Island in Northeast Florida, adjacent to historic Fernandina Beach. Jacksonville Int'l. Airport: 29 miles/47 km, 40 minutes.

Worldwide Reservations
www.preferredhotels.com
800.323.7500 U.S.A./Canada
00.800.3237.5001 Europe (UIFN)
Other areas: *See page 192*

THE LODGE & CLUB AT PONTE VEDRA BEACH

Framed by palm trees and sand dunes, this 10-acre (four-hectare) oceanfront resort sparkles with sophistication and elegance. The Mediterranean-inspired architecture creates the illusion of a charming seaside European village. The soothing sounds of the Atlantic surf set the mood for this warm and inviting atmosphere. Ponte Vedra Beach is a 20-minute drive from Jacksonville. Jacksonville Int'l. Airport: 35 miles/56 km, 40 minutes.

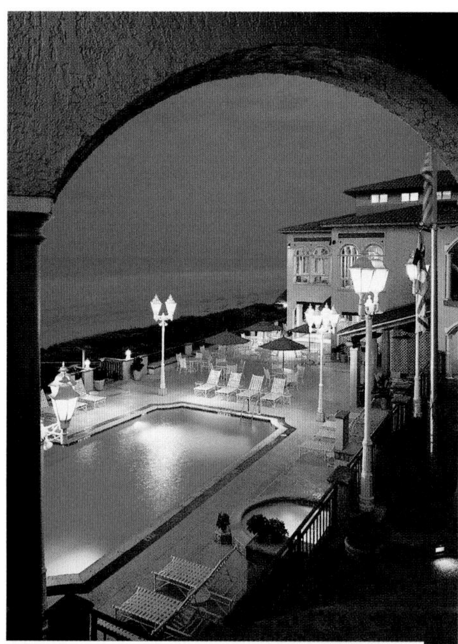

ACCOMMODATIONS: 66 total guestrooms, including 24 suites, each with coffeemaker, Jacuzzi or Roman garden tub, data port, voice mail, newspaper, safe, mini-bar and robes. Some rooms with fireplace. VCR on request.

FACILITIES/SERVICES: Three heated swimming pools, spa, fitness center, concierge, valet parking, high tea daily, child care services, dry cleaning, shoe shine and shops.

BUSINESS SERVICES: On-site Business Center and secretarial services available.

DINING: Dining pleasures include: "The Innlet" for fine dining, "The Ocean Room" and "The Oasis" beachfront patio.

MEETINGS: Total Meeting Rooms: 7
Total Sq. Ft.: 5,680 / Sq. M.: 529

RATES: USD 200.00 to 450.00; Corporate, Group, Package rates.

Mr. Jason D. Smith, Lodge Manager

607 Ponte Vedra Boulevard
Ponte Vedra Beach, Florida 32082, U.S.A.
Tel: +1.904.273.9500
Fax: +1.904.273.0210
Email: reservations@pvresorts.com
www.pvresorts.com

Worldwide Reservations

www.preferredhotels.com
800.323.7500 U.S.A./Canada
00.800.3237.5001 Europe (UIFN)
Other areas: See page 192

MARCO BEACH OCEAN RESORT™

ACCOMMODATIONS: 100 suites, each with full kitchen, separate living room, private balcony, multi-line phones, digital movies/music, data-port, voice mail, complimentary newspaper, safe, mini-bar, hair dryer and robes.

FACILITIES/SERVICES: Spa, Fitness Center, 24-hour concierge, full beach services, dry cleaning, salon and valet parking. Golf and offshore/backwater fishing nearby.

BUSINESS SERVICES: On-site Business Center; executive meeting rooms and secretarial services available.

DINING: "Sale e Pepe" transports guests to Italy with aged stone, marble floors and arabesque walls, and a menu prepared by our native Italian staff. Dine indoors or outdoors under the stars. "Toulouse" is an intimate bar and lounge resembling turn-of-the-century Paris. Pool and beach bar also available.

MEETINGS: Total Meeting Rooms: 2
Total Sq. Ft.: 950 / Sq. M.: 88

RATES: USD 239.00 to 959.00; Corporate, Group, Package rates.

Mr. Joseph Freni,
Acting Managing Director

Antiques and original artwork surround guests with Old World charm reminiscent of the Italian Renaissance. Situated along Marco Island's famous beaches, overlooking the Gulf of Mexico. Superb services and luxurious amenities ensure the ultimate retreat experience. On the Gulf of Mexico, a short drive to Naples. Naples Airport: 18 miles/29 km, 30 minutes. Southwest Florida Int'l. Airport: 51 miles/83 km, 45 minutes.

480 South Collier Blvd.
Marco Island, Florida 34145, U.S.A.
Tel: +1.239.393.1400
Fax: +1.239.393.1401
Email: resmbor@gulfbay.com
www.marcoresort.com

Worldwide Reservations
www.preferredhotels.com
800.323.7500 U.S.A./Canada
00.800.3237.5001 Europe (UIFN)
Other areas: *See page 192*

MAYFAIR HOUSE HOTEL

A unique Art Nouveau-style hotel full of antique and contemporary treasures, the Mayfair House is the focal point of exciting Coconut Grove. Fragrant orchids, flowing spaces, rich stained glass and antique art create the perfect environment for fine dining and elegant functions, both intimate in nature and grand in scale. Mayfair House is located in the center of a tropical bayside village with shopping, dining, museums, art galleries and entertainment. 10 minutes from downtown, the beach and golf. Miami Int'l. Airport: 7 miles/11 km, 10 minutes.

ACCOMMODATIONS: 179 suites, each with either Roman tub or Japanese wooden hot tub on balcony, as well as two multi-line phones, data port, voice mail, CD player, VCR, bathroom TV, newspaper, mini-bar, robes and hair dryer.

FACILITIES/SERVICES: Rooftop pool, Jacuzzi, spa, health club privileges, concierge, dry cleaning, shoe shine, child care services, salon, florist and shops.

BUSINESS SERVICES: On-site Business Center, secretarial and translating services available.

DINING: "The Mayfair Grill" offers a delicious breakfast in an elegant décor of orchids and stained glass; "The Orchid Lounge & Restaurant" offers a selection of wines and a bistro menu.

MEETINGS: Total Meeting Rooms: 10
Total Sq. Ft.: 12,000 / Sq. M.: 1,117

RATES: USD 169.00 to 999.00; Corporate, Group, Package rates.

Mr. Jon Wubbena, General Manager

3000 Florida Avenue
Coconut Grove, Florida 33133, U.S.A.
Tel: +1.305.441.0000
Fax: +1.305.443.4812
Email: mail@mayfairhousehotel.com
www.mayfairhousehotel.com

Worldwide Reservations

www.preferredhotels.com
800.323.7500 U.S.A./Canada
00.800.3237.5001 Europe (UIFN)
Other areas: See page 192

THE PEABODY ORLANDO

ACCOMMODATIONS: 891 total guestrooms, including 57 suites, each with TV in bathroom, data port, voice mail, newspaper, hair dryer, robes and mini-bar; some rooms with CD player. VCR available on request.

FACILITIES/SERVICES: Fitness Center, tennis, concierge, child care services, dry cleaning, shoe shine, salon, shops, massage therapy, golf services and fully stocked Pro Shop. Four lighted, hard-top tennis courts, swimming pool, children's pool, whirlpool, bar and cabana.

BUSINESS SERVICES: On-site Business Center, secretarial and translating services available.

DINING: "Capriccio," classic Northern Italian dishes; "Dux," seasonal haute global cuisine; "B-Line Diner," California cuisine.

MEETINGS: Total Meeting Rooms: 32 Total Sq. Ft.: 57,000 / Sq. M.: 5,307

RATES: USD 390.00 to 1,675.00; Corporate, Group, Package rates.

Mr. Alan Villaverde, Vice President & General Manager

9801 International Drive
Orlando, Florida 32819, U.S.A.
Tel: +1.407.352.4000
Fax: +1.407.351.9177
Email:
peabodyinfo@peabodyorlando.com
www.peabodyorlando.com

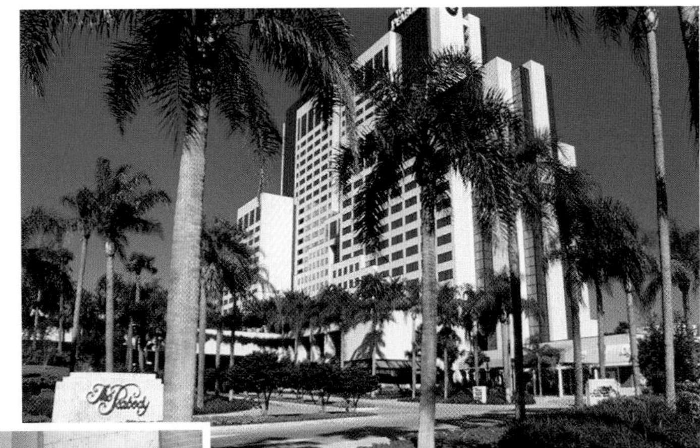

This contemporary hotel is famous for its marble halls, cascading waterfalls, orchids, million-dollar art collection and its famous residents, The Peabody Ducks. Located in the heart of one of the most popular vacation lands, it offers an unparalleled blend of service and Southern elegance to ensure an unforgettable stay. Close to SeaWorld and Discovery Cove, Universal Orlando, Islands of Adventure, Millenium Mall, Pointe Orlando, and across the street from the convention center. Orlando Int'l. Airport: 13 miles/21 km, 20 minutes.

Worldwide Reservations
www.preferredhotels.com
800.323.7500 U.S.A./Canada
00.800.3237.5001 Europe (UIFN)
Other areas: See page 192

CELEBRATION HOTEL

Opened in 1999, this luxury boutique resort in the downtown lakefront community of Celebration features architecture and furnishings reminiscent of early 1900s Florida. Adjacent to Walt Disney World Resort, the resort is situated lakeside in the scenic town of Celebration. A charming, intimate resort that is close to the attractions yet a world away. Orlando Int'l. Airport: 17 miles/27 km, 20 minutes.

ACCOMMODATIONS: 115 total guestrooms, including 6 suites, each with three phones, data port, voice mail, newspaper, safe, hair dryer, make-up mirror, iron and board, and Lodgenet Nintendo.

FACILITIES/SERVICES: The Robert Trent Jones Sr. and Jr. designed Golf Course and the 60,000 sq. ft. Nike Training Center. Fitness Center and Day Spa, concierge services, shoe shine, salon, dry cleaning and shops. Day rental of bikes, scooters and neighborhood electric vehicles.

BUSINESS SERVICES: Secretarial services, translating services, facsimile and copier.

DINING: "The Plantation Room," Old Florida charm, New Florida taste. Continental dining with a hint of Southern flair, "Osceola's," progressive world cuisine served in a club-like atmosphere.

MEETINGS: Total Meeting Rooms: 5 Total Sq. Ft.: 5,000 / Sq. M.: 466

RATES: USD 149.00 to 499.00; Corporate, Group, Package rates.

Mr. Roger Ploum, General Manager

---

700 Bloom Street
Celebration, Florida 34747, U.S.A.
Tel: +1.407.566.6000
Fax: +1.407.566.6001
Email:
reservations@celebrationhotel.com
www.celebrationhotel.com

Worldwide Reservations

www.preferredhotels.com
800.323.7500 U.S.A./Canada
00.800.3237.5001 Europe (UIFN)
Other areas: See page 192

BRAZILIAN COURT HOTEL

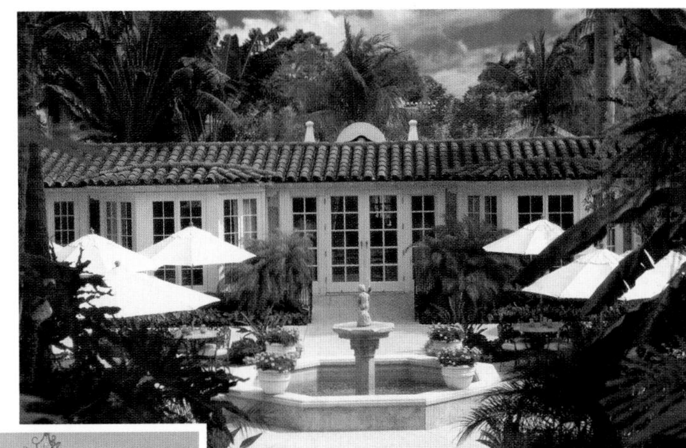

ACCOMMODATIONS: 103 total guestrooms, including 40 suites, each equipped with kitchenette with wet bar, refrigerator, mini-bar, hair dryer, iron and ironing board and coffee-maker. Suites include VCR, CD clock radios and upgraded amenities.

FACILITIES/SERVICES: Fitness center, salon, secluded pool, valet parking, twice daily housekeeping and nightly turn-down.

BUSINESS SERVICES: Copying, typing, translations, currency exchange, computer rental, Internet access and notary public available.

DINING: Celebrated New York chef Daniel Boulud will open his second "Café Boulud" in Palm Beach at the Brazilian Court in January 2003. The concept will be traditional, contemporary and seasonal French cuisine in a casually elegant setting.

MEETINGS: Total Meeting Rooms: 4
Total Sq. Ft.: 1,872 / Sq. M.: 174

RATES: USD 315.00 to 1,025.00; Corporate, Group, Package rates.

Mr. Mathew Pargament,
General Manager

 @

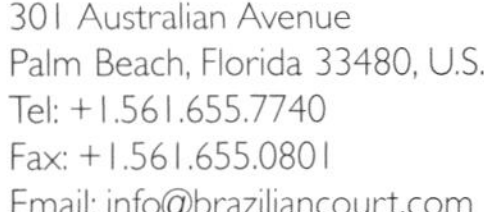

301 Australian Avenue
Palm Beach, Florida 33480, U.S.A.
Tel: +1.561.655.7740
Fax: +1.561.655.0801
Email: info@braziliancourt.com
www.braziliancourt.com

A haven of tranquility for visitors who seek understated elegance and personal service, the historic Brazilian Court is just steps from the world-class shopping of Worth Avenue and a short stroll from the beaches of the beautiful blue Atlantic Ocean. Tucked away on a quiet tree-lined street in the heart of Palm Beach, Brazilian Court remains a charming oasis for discerning travelers. Located steps from the Atlantic beaches, shops, museums, galleries and other recreational activities. Palm Beach Int'l. Airport: 4 miles/6 km, 15 minutes.

Worldwide Reservations
www.preferredhotels.com
800.323.7500 U.S.A./Canada
00.800.3237.5001 Europe (UIFN)
Other areas: See page 192

THE CASA MONICA HOTEL

Built in 1888 and restored to all its grandeur in 1999, this boutique hotel offers the rarest combination of luxury and history. The castle, designed in "Spanish Moorish" style, is ideally nestled in the historic district of the oldest city in the United States. Located in downtown St. Augustine, within walking distance to museums, restaurants, shops and attractions. Transportation and car rentals available. Jacksonville Int'l. Airport: 50 miles/81 km, 50 minutes; Orlando Int'l. Airport: 90 miles/145 km, 90 minutes.

ACCOMMODATIONS: 138 total guestrooms, including 14 suites, each with three multi-line phones, data port, voice mail, complimentary newspaper, safe, robes and hair dryer. Refrigerators in some rooms.

FACILITIES/SERVICES: Serenata Beach Club, spa services, fitness center, concierge, shoe shine, child care services and shops. More than 20 golf courses nearby.

BUSINESS SERVICES: Complimentary Business Center and secretarial services.

DINING: "95 Cordova," St. Augustine's only Four-Star restaurant, serves the freshest, most unique dishes in Florida. The award-winning restaurant is popular with locals and hotel guests alike. Private Wine Rooms available for special occasions. "The Gourmet European Market" serves cappuccino, sandwiches, pastries and desserts.

MEETINGS: Total Meeting Rooms: 8 Total Sq. Ft.: 15,000 / Sq. M.: 1,396

RATES: USD 129.00 to 999.00; Corporate, Group, Package rates.

Mr. Troy S. Bennett CHA,
General Manager

---

95 Cordova Street
St. Augustine, Florida 32084, U.S.A.
Tel: +1.904.827.1888
Fax: +1.904.819.6065
Email:
casamonica@grandthemehotels.com
www.casamonica.com

Worldwide Reservations

www.preferredhotels.com
800.323.7500 U.S.A./Canada
00.800.3237.5001 Europe (UIFN)
Other areas: See page 192

CHÂTEAU ÉLAN WINERY & RESORT

ACCOMMODATIONS: 209 total guestrooms, including 17 suites, each with three phones, data port, voice mail, newspaper, mini-bar, robes, hair dryer, sunken tub and walk-in shower. VCR available on request.

FACILITIES/SERVICES: Championship Golf, European-style spa, four pools, seven tennis courts, equestrian center, performance driving school, winery tours and tastings, nature trails and Kids Club. Concierge, fitness center, child care services and dry cleaning.

BUSINESS SERVICES: Business Center and secretarial services.

DINING: Eight unique dining options, ranging from the wine-paired menus of "Le Clos" and the casual bistro fare at "Café Élan" to the health-inspired dishes of "Fleur-de-Lis."

MEETINGS: Total Meeting Rooms: 29 Total Sq. Ft.: 38,000 / Sq. M.: 3,538

RATES: USD 119.00 to 250.00; Corporate, Group, Package rates.

Mr. Henk Evers, President & CEO

---

100 Rue Charlemagne
Braselton, Georgia 30517, U.S.A.
Tel: +1.678.425.0900
Fax: +1.678.425.6000
Email: info@chateauelan.com
www.chateauelan.com

An elegant 16th-century-style French chateau and winery set on 3,500 acres (1,416 hectares) of rolling hills surrounded by lush vineyards. The French country estate setting enriched with Southern hospitality provides a unique resort experience with challenging golf, tennis, a spa and superb restaurants. Located just north of Atlanta, immediately off Interstate 85. Hartsfield Int'l Airport: 50 miles/ 81 km, 50 minutes.

Worldwide Reservations
www.preferredhotels.com
800.323.7500 U.S.A./Canada
00.800.3237.5001 Europe (UIFN)
Other areas: See page 192

HALEKULANI

Lending elegance to the past, this modern hotel has retained much of its original 1930s charm and graciousness. Halekulani delivers understated luxury in an oasis of tranquility in the heart of Waikiki. Fine cuisine awaits guests at this luxurious paradise, where stellar service is standard. On Waikiki Beach, an easy walk to the Waikiki shopping district. Honolulu Int'l. Airport: 9 miles/14 km, 25 minutes. Hawaii Convention Center: 1 mile/2 km.

ACCOMMODATIONS: 456 total guestrooms, including 44 suites, each with balcony, three phones, fax modem service, complimentary local calls, fruit basket, newspaper, separate shower and soaking tub.

FACILITIES/SERVICES: Fitness center, concierge, child care services, dry cleaning, business center, salon, spa, florist and shops. Complimentary tickets to Oahu's cultural venues.

BUSINESS SERVICES: On-site Business Center; secretarial services, personal computers, Internet, fax and copy machines available.

DINING: Enjoy "La Mer" for exquisite Neo-classic French cuisine, "Orchids" for contemporary seafood or "House Without a Key" for casual dining and nightly Hawaiian entertainment.

MEETINGS: Total Meeting Rooms: 5 Total Sq. Ft.: 8,454 / Sq. M.: 787

RATES: USD 325.00 to 4,500.00; Group, Package rates.

Mr. Fred Honda, General Manager

2199 Kalia Road
Honolulu, Hawaii 96815, U.S.A.
Tel: +1.808.923.2311
Fax: +1.808.926.8004
Email: reservations@halekulani.com
www.halekulani.com

Worldwide Reservations
www.preferredhotels.com
800.323.7500 U.S.A./Canada
00.800.3237.5001 Europe (UIFN)
Other areas: See page 192

GET THE "GREEN CARPET TREATMENT" AT PREFERRED'S GOLF RESORTS

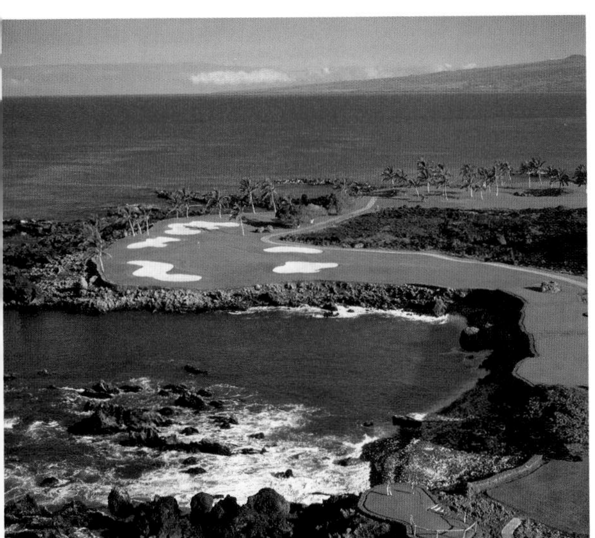

SPECTACULAR VIEWS. CHALLENGING courses by world-renowned designers. Unique programs. All are part of the "green-carpet treatment" offered at Preferred golf resorts. Experience *Ke'ano Kolepa* — the Spirit of Golf — at **Mauna Lani Bay Hotel & Bungalows,** where tai-chi, meditation and a spa treatment put you in the Zen of golf. Learn from the best at **Palazzo Arzaga Hotel, Spa & Golf Resort**, featuring an 18-hole Jack Nicklaus II course, nine-hole Gary Player course, and Arzaga Golf Academy, a European PGA teaching and learning center. An ancient mahogany grove overlooking a gorgeous crescent of beach on Barbados' western coast is the setting for The Old Nine, the Tom Fazio-designed Country Club Course and the spectacular Green Monkey Course at **Sandy Lane.** Perched on 520 acres of a spectacular cliff formation, **St Andrew's Bay Golf Resort and Spa** sports two championship golf courses offering breathtaking panoramic views of the Fife countryside and nearby St Andrews.

For more information on a Preferred golf experience, refer to page 192 for a local reservation number or visit our Web site at www.preferredhotels.com.

MAUNA LANI BAY HOTEL & BUNGALOWS

ACCOMMODATIONS: 350 total guestrooms, including 15 suites, each with two phones, data port, voice mail, VCR, safe, mini-bar and robes.

FACILITIES/SERVICES: Mauna Lani Spa, fitness center with lap pool, 36 holes of golf, 16 tennis courts, ocean sports, pool, concierge, children's camp, child care services, salon, florist and shops.

BUSINESS SERVICES: On-site Business Center, Internet access, secretarial and translating services available.

DINING: "Canoe House," Pacific Rim cuisine; "Bay Terrace," Mediterranean cuisine; "Gallery," American fare; "Ocean Grill," poolside dining; "Honu Bar," light dinners and appetizers.

MEETINGS: Total Meeting Rooms: 8
Total Sq. Ft.: 7,800 / Sq. M.: 726

RATES: USD 375.00 to 4,900.00; Corporate, Group, Package rates.

Mr. Kurt Matsumoto, Vice President

68-1400 Mauna Lani Drive
Kohala Coast, Hawaii 96743, U.S.A.
Tel: +1.808.885.6622
Fax: +1.808.885.1484
Email: reservations@maunalani.com
www.maunalani.com

Mauna Lani embodies the theme "Spirit of Place" with its acres of ancient fishponds and cultural activities. This luxurious ocean-front resort is an exquisite blend of under-stated elegance, superb cuisine, the new Mauna Lani Spa and world-class golf. Relax in an intimate surrounding enriched with Hawaiian aloha. Beachfront on the sunny Kohala Coast of the Big Island. Shopping and dining nearby and 20 minutes to the town of Waimea. Kona Int'l. Airport: 25 miles/40 km, 25 minutes.

Worldwide Reservations
www.preferredhotels.com
800.323.7500 U.S.A./Canada
00.800.3237.5001 Europe (UIFN)
Other areas: See page 192

THE PENINSULA CHICAGO

The classical limestone structure of The Peninsula Chicago reflects both the city's signature modern architecture and the elegance of neighboring buildings on North Michigan Avenue from the 1930s. Guests will enjoy luxurious accommodations, a spectacular glass-enclosed ballroom and The Terrace, which overlooks the "Magnificent Mile." Ideally located on North Michigan Avenue. O'Hare Int'l. Airport: 20 miles/32 km, 35 minutes.

ACCOMMODATIONS: 339 total guestrooms, including 83 suites, each with four multi-line phones, data port, voice mail, fax, Internet access, mini-bar, televisions and robes in all bathrooms. Suites with VCR and CD Player.

FACILITIES/SERVICES: The Peninsula Spa, with city views, occupies the top two floors of the hotel. Fully equipped fitness center, an 82-foot (25-meter) swimming pool, Jacuzzi, treatment rooms and sun deck.

BUSINESS SERVICES: Business Center with private offices and separate workstations.

DINING: For fine dining, "Avenues" specializes in "cuisine de la mer," while "Shanghai Terrace" offers Asian dishes. "Pierrot Gourmet," for casual dining, is reminiscent of a European cafe. "The Lobby" provides elegant all-day dining and afternoon tea. "The Bar" features a port and cigar collection.

MEETINGS: Total Meeting Rooms: 8
Total Sq. Ft.: 19,000 / Sq. M.: 1,769

RATES: USD 395.00 to 4,700.00; Corporate, Group, Package rates.

Mrs. Maria Razumich-Zec,
General Manager

108 East Superior Street
Chicago, Illinois 60611, U.S.A.
Tel: +1.312.337.2888
Fax: +1.312.751.2888
Email: pch@peninsula.com
www.peninsula.com

Worldwide Reservations
www.preferredhotels.com
800.323.7500 U.S.A./Canada
00.800.3237.5001 Europe (UIFN)
Other areas: See page 192

CANTERBURY HOTEL

ACCOMMODATIONS: 99 total guestrooms, including 25 suites, each with two phones, data port, voice mail, newspaper, mini-bar, hair-dryer and robes. CD player and VCR available on request.

FACILITIES/SERVICES: Fitness room, concierge, dry cleaning, shoe shine, complimentary continental breakfast, turndown service with chocolate truffles and 24-hour room service.

BUSINESS SERVICES: Secretarial and translating services available. Limo service available Monday-Friday, 7 to 8:30 a.m.

DINING: The award-winning "Restaurant at the Canterbury" features American and Continental cuisine in an elegant, intimate setting. Afternoon tea is served daily at 4 p.m.

MEETINGS: Total Meeting Rooms: 5 Total Sq. Ft.: 2,673 / Sq. M.: 249

RATES: USD 225.00 to 1,575.00; Corporate, Group, Package rates.

Mrs. Letitia Moscrip,
General Manager

123 South Illinois Street
Indianapolis, Indiana 46225, U.S.A.
Tel: +1.317.634.3000
Fax: +1.317.685.2519
Email: info@canterburyhotel.com
www.canterburyhotel.com

An intimate European-style hotel with Queen Anne and Chippendale-style furnishings, marble floors, imported cherrywood and an elegant two-story atrium. Nestled in the heart of downtown Indianapolis, this Historic Landmark provides direct access to Circle Centre Mall via skywalk on the Mezzanine level. Located on the historic Illinois Street block next to the famous St. Elmo Steakhouse and near entertainment and dining facilities. Indianapolis Int'l. Airport: 8 miles/13 km, 15 minutes.

Worldwide Reservations
www.preferredhotels.com
800.323.7500 U.S.A./Canada
00.800.3237.5001 Europe (UIFN)
Other areas: See page 192

LE PAVILLON HOTEL

ACCOMMODATIONS: 226 total guestrooms, including 7 suites, each with three multi-line phones, data port, voice mail, newspaper, safe, mini-bar, robes and high-speed Internet access.

FACILITIES/SERVICES: Fitness center, concierge, child care services, dry cleaning, shoe shine, valet parking, heated pool and whirlpool.

BUSINESS SERVICES: High-speed Internet access available in meeting facilities and translating services available.

DINING: "Crystal Room" offers New Orleans cuisine, full breakfast, a salad and pasta bar, along with full menu selections for lunch and dinner served nightly. "Gallery Lounge" offers light fare. 24-hour in-room dining also available.

MEETINGS: Total Meeting Rooms: 8
Total Sq. Ft.: 9,063 / Sq. M.: 844

RATES: USD 230.00 to 3,000.00; Corporate, Group, Package rates.

Mr. Edward P. Morin,
Managing Director

---

833 Poydras Street
New Orleans, Louisiana 70112, U.S.A.
Tel: +1.504.581.3111
Fax: +1.504.620.4130
Email: sales@lepavillon.com
www.lepavillon.com

The "Belle of New Orleans," built in 1907, is a completely restored, full-service hotel located in the heart of New Orleans. Guests can enjoy the elegance and history of New Orleans with each stay at Le Pavillon Hotel. Conveniently located near the Convention Center, Superdome, riverfront attractions and French Quarter. New Orleans Int'l. Airport: 13 miles/21 km, 30 minutes.

Worldwide Reservations
www.preferredhotels.com
800.323.7500 U.S.A./Canada
00.800.3237.5001 Europe (UIFN)
Other areas: See page 192

HARBOR COURT HOTEL

Decorated like the home of a well-traveled English explorer, Harbor Court offers European style and elegance with modern amenities. Guests can relax in luxurious surroundings and enjoy the pampering of an attentive staff. Overlooks the Inner Harbor within close proximity of the National Aquarium, Harborplace, Oriole Park and Ravens Stadium. Baltimore-Washington Int'l. Airport: 8 miles/13 km, 15 minutes.

ACCOMMODATIONS: 195 total guestrooms, including 21 suites, each with three multi-line phones, high-speed Internet access, voice mail, fax, CD player, newspaper, mini-bar, hair dryer and robes. VCR on request.

FACILITIES/SERVICES: Racquetball, yoga, fitness center, tennis, concierge, child care services, dry cleaning, shoe shine, massage & facial treatments, florist and parking garage.

BUSINESS SERVICES: On-site Business Center; secretarial and translating services and high-speed Internet access in meeting rooms available.

DINING: The award winning "Hampton's" features seasonal American cuisine. "Café Brightons" offers casual dining. For cocktails, cigars and live jazz, try "Explorers Lounge."

MEETINGS: Total Meeting Rooms: 9 Total Sq. Ft.: 7,700 / Sq. M.: 717

RATES: USD 245.00 to 4,000.00; Corporate, Group, Package rates.

Mr. Werner R. Kunz,
Managing Director

550 Light Street
Baltimore, Maryland 21202, U.S.A.
Tel: +1.410.234.0550
Fax: +1.410.659.5925
Email: harbor@harborcourt.com
www.harborcourt.com

Worldwide Reservations
www.preferredhotels.com
800.323.7500 U.S.A./Canada
00.800.3237.5001 Europe (UIFN)
Other areas: See page 192

THE INN AT PERRY CABIN

ACCOMMODATIONS: 81 total guestrooms, including 27 suites, each with mineral waters, VCR, data port, newspaper and robes.

FACILITIES/SERVICES: Pool, bar lounge, bicycles, boating, fitness center, concierge, child care services, dry cleaning and shoe shine.

BUSINESS SERVICES: Secretarial services, fax and computer available.

DINING: The restaurant "Sherwood Landing" features excellent food based on the riches of the locality, fresh fish and Chesapeake specialties mixed with fine international fare. Afternoon tea offered daily with a selection of homemade English scones, preserves and more.

MEETINGS: Total Meeting Rooms: 6 Total Sq. Ft.: 4,434 / Sq. M.: 413

RATES: USD 395.00 to 685.00; Corporate, Group, Package rates.

Mr. Stephen Creese,
General Manager

308 Watkins Lane
St. Michaels, Maryland 21663, U.S.A.
Tel: +1.410.745.2200
Fax: +1.410.745.3348
Email: info@perrycabin.com
www.perrycabin.com

An intimate waterfront resort in a town with handsome churches and manicured Colonial and Victorian-style homes. English and Early American antiques are elegantly offset by classic fabrics, wallpapers and comfortable luxuries creating an atmosphere conducive to relaxation. Within easy reach of Washington, D.C., Baltimore and Philadelphia is St. Michaels, a small town that seems to live in a forgotten era. It slumbers on a beautiful cove off the Chesapeake Bay and is home to the Maritime Museum. Baltimore-Washington Int'l. Airport: 75 miles/121 km, 90 minutes.

Worldwide Reservations
www.preferredhotels.com
800.323.7500 U.S.A./Canada
00.800.3237.5001 Europe (UIFN)
Other areas: See page 192

BOSTON HARBOR HOTEL

ACCOMMODATIONS: 230 total guestrooms, including 26 suites, each room offering multi-line speaker-phones, high-speed Internet access, Web TV, Nintendo, voice mail, mini-bar, newspaper, robes, slippers, umbrella and Molton Brown toiletries. VCR on request.

FACILITIES/SERVICES: Spa, fitness center, indoor pool, concierge, car rental, child care services, dry cleaning, shoe shine, florist, gift shop, valet parking and local towncar service. Pet-friendly accommodations, amenities and dog walking services.

BUSINESS SERVICES: Business Center, Internet access, computer stations, secretarial and translating services.

DINING: At "Meritage – The Restaurant" experience the fusion of food and wine, boasting spectacular harbor views; "Intrigue Cafe" for casual indoor and seasonal outdoor dining; and "Rowes Wharf Bar" for cocktails and lighter fare.

MEETINGS: Total Meeting Rooms: 9
Total Sq. Ft.: 15,000 / Sq. M.: 1,396

RATES: USD 325.00 to 1,900.00; Corporate, Group, Package rates.

Mr. Paul Jacques, General Manager

Rowes Wharf
Boston, Massachusetts 02110, U.S.A.
Tel: +1.617.439.7000
Fax: +1.617.330.9450
Email: reservations@bhh.com
www.bhh.com

The waterfront hotel's 80-foot (24-meter) arch and glass-domed rotunda are complemented by hand-carved wood, Italian marble and historic art. Yachts and sailboats glide on the harbor of this landmark hotel. Warm service welcomes guests to unforgettable comfort, style and elegance. "Boston's Best Hotel" by *Boston Magazine* for 2002 and rated as "One of the Top 100 Places to Stay" by *Condé Nast Traveler*. In the Financial District near museums, theaters and shopping. Logan Int'l. Airport: 1 mile/2 km, 10 minutes. Airport Water Shuttle: 0.5 miles/1 km, 7 minutes.

Worldwide Reservations
www.preferredhotels.com
800.323.7500 U.S.A./Canada
00.800.3237.5001 Europe (UIFN)
Other areas: See page 192

FIFTEEN BEACON

A refined landmark hotel in a 1903 Beaux Arts building that juxtaposes cutting-edge technology with extraordinary Jeffersonian styling. Located across from the Boston Common and blocks from the waterfront, this striking cosmopolitan hotel offers a rarefied residential atmosphere. Situated atop historic Beacon Hill and central to the Financial District, the State House and exclusive Newbury Street. Logan Int'l. Airport: 5 miles/8 km, 15 minutes.

ACCOMMODATIONS: 60 total guestrooms, including 3 suites, each with three multi-line phones, data port, voice mail, fax, working gas fireplace, newspaper, CD player, safe, mini-bar and robes.

FACILITIES/SERVICES: Fitness center, concierge, dry cleaning, shoe shine and in-town chauffeured Mercedes sedan service.

BUSINESS SERVICES: Secretarial and translating services, in-room direct high-speed Internet access, personalized business cards with private DID line and fax number.

DINING: "The Federalist Restaurant" is a culinary destination with an atmosphere allusive of the world's most prestigious clubs. The signature of "The Fed" is Boston's most extensive wine cellar.

MEETINGS: Total Meeting Rooms: 2
Total Sq. Ft.: 1,175 / Sq. M.: 109

RATES: USD 395.00 to 2,500.00; Corporate, Group, Package rates.

Mr. William J. Sander III,
General Manager

15 Beacon Street
Boston, Massachusetts 02108, U.S.A.
Tel: +1.617.670.1500
Fax: +1.617.670.2525
Email: hotel@xvbeacon.com
www.xvbeacon.com

Worldwide Reservations
www.preferredhotels.com
800.323.7500 U.S.A./Canada
00.800.3237.5001 Europe (UIFN)
Other areas: See page 192

THE CHARLES HOTEL, HARVARD SQUARE

ACCOMMODATIONS: 293 total guestrooms, including 44 suites, each with Internet access, three multi-line phones, voice mail, mini-bar, robes and slippers, TV in all bathrooms and DVD player and radio. Views include the Boston skyline.

FACILITIES/SERVICES: Tri-level fitness center with indoor pool, spa, concierge, dry cleaning and multi-lingual staff.

BUSINESS SERVICES: On-site Business Center, audio-visual consultant and administrative services available.

DINING: Award-winning "Rialto" serves Mediterranean fusion cuisine. "Henrietta's Table" offers New England classics using fresh local ingredients. Live jazz at "Regattabar." "Noir" is perfect for cocktails.

MEETINGS: Total Meeting Rooms: 18
Total Sq. Ft.: 13,300 / Sq. M.: 1,209

RATES: USD 250.00 to 599.00; Corporate, Group, Package rates.

Mr. Paul Giovanini, General Manager

Known as Boston's most original hotel, The Charles Hotel is simple, stylish and smart. Situated in the heart of Harvard Square, the intellectual center of the nation, The Charles offers modern décor in a historic yet energetic setting. Four blocks to the gates of Harvard Yard, and one block from the Charles River. Less than 10 minutes to Boston by car or subway. Logan Int'l. Airport: 7 miles/11 km, 15 minutes.

One Bennett Street/Harvard Square
Cambridge, Massachusetts 02138, U.S.A.
Tel: +1.617.864.1200
Fax: +1.617.864.5715
Email: reservations@charleshotel.com
www.charleshotel.com

Worldwide Reservations
www.preferredhotels.com
800.323.7500 U.S.A./Canada
00.800.3237.5001 Europe (UIFN)
Other areas: See page 192

WEQUASSETT INN RESORT AND GOLF CLUB

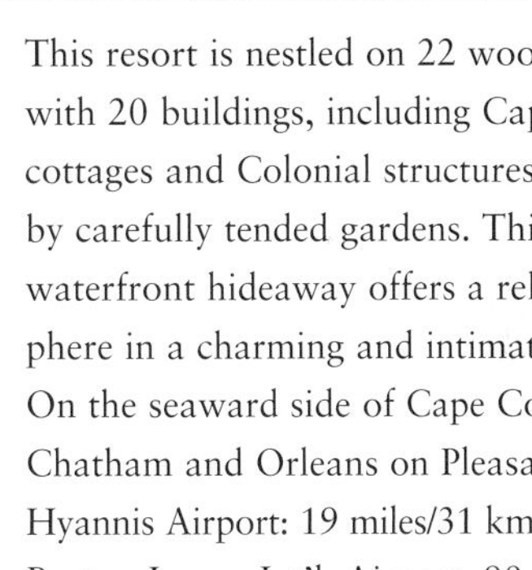

ACCOMMODATIONS: 104 total guestrooms, including 8 suites, each with balcony or patio, data port, voice mail, coffeemaker, newspaper and VCR on request.

FACILITIES/SERVICES: 18-hole golf course, pool, boating, croquet, volleyball, basketball, shuffleboard, horseshoes, fitness center, tennis, child care services, dry cleaning, concierge and shops.

BUSINESS SERVICES: Secretarial services available.

DINING: "Twenty-Eight Atlantic," a new elegant waterfront restaurant serving Progressive New England cuisine. "Thoreau's," a warm and intimate lounge. "The Outer Bar & Grille" offers an informal yet distinctive setting overlooking the bay.

MEETINGS: Total Meeting Rooms: 12
Total Sq. Ft.: 6,120 / Sq. M.: 570

RATES: USD 225.00 to 1,100.00; Group, Package rates.

Mr. Mark J. Novota,
Managing Partner

On Pleasant Bay
Chatham, Massachusetts 02633, U.S.A.
Tel: +1.508.432.5400
Fax: +1.508.432.5032
Email: fkiernan@wequassett.com
www.wequassett.com

This resort is nestled on 22 wooded acres with 20 buildings, including Cape Cod-style cottages and Colonial structures surrounded by carefully tended gardens. This secluded waterfront hideaway offers a relaxing atmosphere in a charming and intimate setting. On the seaward side of Cape Cod between Chatham and Orleans on Pleasant Bay. Hyannis Airport: 19 miles/31 km, 20 minutes. Boston Logan Int'l. Airport: 90 miles/ 145 km, 90 minutes.

Worldwide Reservations
www.preferredhotels.com
800.323.7500 U.S.A./Canada
00.800.3237.5001 Europe (UIFN)
Other areas: See page 192

THE ORCHARDS HOTEL

This intimate hotel, built around a peaceful courtyard with reflecting pool, fragrant blooms and stunning statuary, surrounds you with comfort. Nestled in the Berkshire Mountains, this hotel offers a tranquil refuge in America's Premier Cultural Resort. Experience the attentive staff and serene elegance evocative of a gracious country estate. Conveniently near the theater, museums, golf and Tanglewood. Three hours from Boston or New York City. Albany Int'l. Airport: 50 miles/80 km, 45 minutes.

Worldwide Reservations
www.preferredhotels.com
800.323.7500 U.S.A./Canada
00.800.3237.5001 Europe (UIFN)
Other areas: See page 192

ACCOMMODATIONS: 49 total guestrooms, including 2 suites, some with fireplaces, each including two multi-line phones, data port, voice mail, VCR and robes.

FACILITIES/SERVICES: Fitness center, concierge, child care services, swimming pool, environmental chamber, bicycles and sauna.

BUSINESS SERVICES: Secretarial services available.

DINING: The award-winning "Yasmin's Restaurant" offers a sophisticated blend of international cuisine and classic New England favorites. "The Lounge" serves cocktails and light fare in a comfortable, relaxed atmosphere, and the "Courtyard" is a peaceful setting for alfresco dining. Visits to the Private Cellar may be made by appointment and are a special treat for wine lovers.

MEETINGS: Total Meeting Rooms: 4
Total Sq. Ft.: 2,700 / Sq. M.: 251

RATES: USD 195.00 to 275.00; Corporate, Group, Package rates.

Mr. Sayed M. Saleh,
Managing Director

222 Adams Road
Williamstown, Massachusetts 01267, U.S.A.
Tel: +1.413.458.9611
Fax: +1.413.458.3273
Email: the-orchards@worldnet.att.net
www.orchardshotel.com

THE TOWNSEND HOTEL

Known as the locale of choice for metropolitan Detroit's affluent traveler, The Townsend is nestled among the tree-lined streets, shops and restaurants in this boutique suburban community. The beauty of the hotel lobby's Waterford chandeliers, flowers and marble fireplace is surpassed by the attention to detail by the award-winning hotel staff. The Townsend exudes charm and elegance. Located 20 minutes north of downtown. Detroit Metropolitan Airport: 25 miles/ 40 km, 40 minutes. Pontiac/Oakland County Airport: 20 miles/32 km, 30 minutes.

ACCOMMODATIONS: 150 total guestrooms, including 55 suites, and 2 penthouse suites, all with interactive cable TV, Internet access, multi-line cordless phone with data port and voice mail, CD player, refreshment center and oversized safe. European bed linens, bathrobe and slippers, newspaper and coffee service for each room. Complimentary VCR and fax machines upon request.

FACILITIES/SERVICES: Fitness center, concierge, walking distance to the area's finest restaurants, shopping and spas.

BUSINESS SERVICES: High-speed Internet connection, Business Center with Internet workstations, scanner, color printer and high-speed copier.

DINING: Award-winning "The Rugby Grille" offers breakfast, lunch and dinner daily. Eclectic nightspot "The Corner."

MEETINGS: Total Meeting Rooms: 7
Total Sq. Ft.: 9,300 / Sq. M.: 866

RATES: USD 275.00 to 1,500.00; Corporate, Group, Package rates.

Mr. Peter Wilde, Managing Director

---

100 Townsend Street
Birmingham, Michigan 48009, U.S.A.
Tel: +1.248.642.7900
Fax: +1.248.645.9061
Email: reservations@townsendhotel.com
www.townsendhotel.com

Worldwide Reservations
www.preferredhotels.com
800.323.7500 U.S.A./Canada
00.800.3237.5001 Europe (UIFN)
Other areas: See page 192

THE GRAND HOTEL MINNEAPOLIS

Recently restored, this turn-of-the-century building is now home to The Grand Hotel Minneapolis. With its marble and mahogany-paneled lobby, guests can enjoy an intimate, luxurious experience in the heart of Minneapolis. Centrally located in the business and financial district of downtown Minneapolis. Within walking distance and skyway-connected to theaters, shopping and entertainment. Minneapolis-St. Paul Int'l. Airport: 12 miles/20 km, 15 minutes.

Worldwide Reservations
www.preferredhotels.com
800.323.7500 U.S.A./Canada
00.800.3237.5001 Europe (UIFN)
Other areas: See page 192

ACCOMMODATIONS: 140 total guestrooms, including 17 suites, wrapped in creamy neutrals, each with radio/CD players, high-speed Internet connection, two-line speaker phones, data port, voice mail, in-room safes, mini-bar, down comforters, bathrobes, soaking tubs and many with TVs in bathroom.

FACILITIES/SERVICES: World-Class 58,000-square-foot (5,400-square-meter) state-of-the-art athletic facility with spa, pool, squash courts, gymnasium, racquetball and handball courts.

BUSINESS SERVICES: Business Center featuring private offices.

DINING: Three in-house restaurants: "Martini BLU," offering dining and entertainment, an award-winning sushi bar, a deli and a classic lobby bar.

MEETINGS: Total Meeting Rooms: 7
Total Sq. Ft.: 8,000 / Sq. M.: 745

RATES: USD 249.00 to 3,500.00; Corporate, Group, Package rates.

Mr. Mark Peregory, Vice President & Managing Director

---

615 Second Avenue South
Minneapolis, Minnesota 55402, U.S.A.
Tel: +1.612.288.8888
Fax: +1.612.373.0407
Email: info@grandhotelminneapolis.com
www.grandhotelminneapolis.com

HOTEL PHILLIPS

ACCOMMODATIONS: 215 total guestrooms, including 2 suites, each with two multi-line phones, voice mail, data port, newspaper, robes, coffeemaker. Fax machine on request.

FACILITIES/SERVICES: Fitness center, concierge, shoe shine and dry cleaning.

BUSINESS SERVICES: Business Center and secretarial services.

DINING: Adding to the guest experience are two diverse restaurants, each offering an outstanding dining experience. "Platters" is one of the highlights of the renovation with its historic ambiance, unique service concept and exquisitely prepared food. "12 Baltimore" is the perfect destination for lunch and dinner, and offers a near-perfect mix of top food and drink. It's downtown's place to see and be seen.

MEETINGS: Total Meeting Rooms: 8
Total Sq. Ft.: 5,668 / Sq. M.: 528

RATES: USD 129.00 to 219.00; Corporate, Group, Package rates.

Mr. Tom Pratt, General Manager

---

106 West 12th Street
Kansas City, Missouri 64105, U.S.A.
Tel: +1.816.221.7000
Fax: +1.816.221.3477
Email: tinaharlow@hotelphillips.com
www.hotelphillips.com

Hotel Phillips is a historical landmark that combines Art Deco ambiance with European-style luxury in the heart of downtown Kansas City. This contemporary yet inviting hotel creates an intimate refuge for today's business or leisure traveler. Hotel Phillips is ideally located two blocks from the Convention Center. Kansas City Int'l. Airport: 17 miles/28 km, 25 minutes. Downtown Executive Airport: .5 miles/ 1 km, 10 minutes.

Worldwide Reservations
www.preferredhotels.com
800.323.7500 U.S.A./Canada
00.800.3237.5001 Europe (UIFN)
Other areas: See page 192

CLAYTON ON THE PARK, A HOTEL & RESIDENCE

This cosmopolitan hotel combines modern amenities with Midwestern hospitality. The modern lobby is accented with a giant saltwater aquarium housing a live coral reef, as well as an intimate sitting area with a warm glowing fireplace. Overlooking Shaw Park and its outdoor pools and tennis courts, Clayton on the Park is within walking distance to businesses, specialty stores, antique shops, art galleries and restaurants. Near the area's largest shopping center and attractions, Clayton is the business and social hub of the metropolitan St. Louis region. Lambert Int'l. Airport: 15 miles/24 km, 15 minutes.

ACCOMMODATIONS: 98 suites, each with a fully stocked kitchen, two multi-line phones, data port, voice mail, caller ID, newspaper, personal mini-bar shopping list, robes, hair dryer, magnified make-up mirror, full kitchen, and coffeemaker, toasters and VCRs are available on request.

FACILITIES/SERVICES: Nutriformance Fitness Center, rooftop Veranda with 360-degree views, concierge, nanny services available and dry cleaning. Swimming, tennis and ice-skating available across the street in Shaw Park, as well as extensive fitness facilities and two indoor pools.

BUSINESS SERVICES: Business Center and secretarial services, conference rooms, high-speed Internet wireless access and private offices.

DINING: Baseball Hall of Famer Ozzie Smith and Chef David Slay's "Smith & Slay's Restaurant and Bon Bar."

MEETINGS: Total Meeting Rooms: 6
Total Sq. Ft.: 10,833 / Sq. M.: 1,009

RATES: USD 155.00 to 300.00; Group, Package rates.

Mr. Micarl Hill, General Manager

8025 Bonhomme Avenue
Clayton, Missouri 63105, U.S.A.
Tel: +1.314.721.6543
Fax: +1.314.721.8588
Email:
reservations@claytononthepark.com
www.claytononthepark.com

Worldwide Reservations

www.preferredhotels.com
800.323.7500 U.S.A./Canada
00.800.3237.5001 Europe (UIFN)
Other areas: *See page 192*

INN OF THE ANASAZI

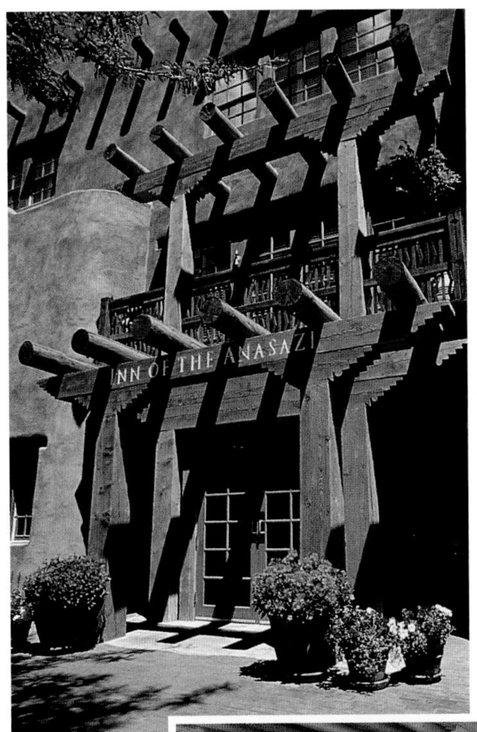

An intimate and romantic world-class inn and restaurant featuring traditional Pueblo-style architecture, authentic artwork and four-poster beds. Nestled in the heart of Santa Fe's historic district, the Inn is a haven for travelers. Located just steps from Santa Fe's Plaza at the base of the Sangre de Cristo Mountains. Golf, horseback riding, spa, Anasazi ruins, museums and other outdoor activities are nearby. Albuquerque Int'l. Airport: 60 miles/97 km, 75 minutes.

ACCOMMODATIONS: 59 total guestrooms, including 8 deluxe rooms, each with a gaslit fireplace, two phones, data port, voice mail, VCR, newspaper, safe, mini-bar, robes, coffee and iron and ironing board.

FACILITIES/SERVICES: Room service, concierge, child care services, dry cleaning and shoe shine.

BUSINESS SERVICES: The front desk can take care of most business needs. Computers, Internet access, etc., are available for an hourly rental charge.

DINING: The "Anasazi Restaurant" features award-winning Southwestern cuisine for breakfast, lunch and dinner.

MEETINGS: Total Meeting Rooms: 2 Total Sq. Ft.: 825 / Sq. M.: 77

RATES: USD 199.00 to 469.00

Mr. Jeff Mahan, General Manager

---

113 Washington Avenue
Santa Fe, New Mexico 87501, U.S.A.
Tel: +1.505.988.3030
Fax: +1.505.988.3277
Email:
reservations@innoftheanasazi.com
www.innoftheanasazi.com

Worldwide Reservations

www.preferredhotels.com
800.323.7500 U.S.A./Canada
00.800.3237.5001 Europe (UIFN)
Other areas: See page 192

THE SAGAMORE

Situated in the unspoiled Adirondack Mountains, The Sagamore is a private island resort on Lake George in upstate New York. Guests enjoy comfortable accommodations in the Historic Hotel and the Adirondack-style Lodges and a choice of dining at six extraordinary restaurants. The Sagamore, which features a Donald Ross championship golf course and European-style spa, is a year-round sports paradise. At Bolton Landing, on its own 72-acre island. Albany Int'l. Airport: 65 miles/105 km, 75 minutes.

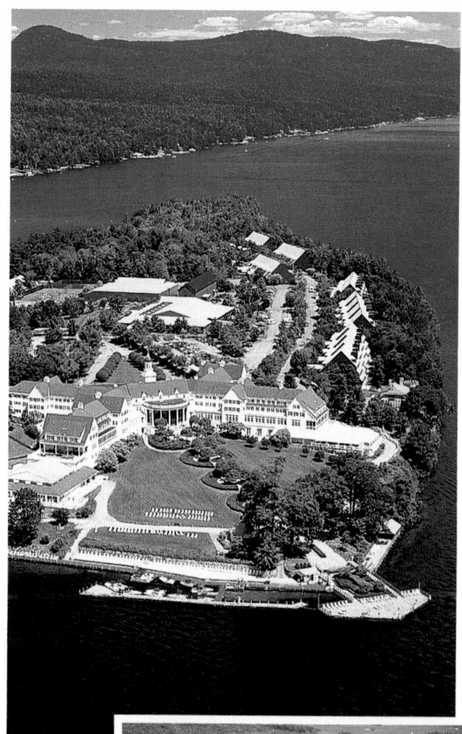

ACCOMMODATIONS: 350 total guestrooms, including 176 suites, with lake view and garden view rooms. The Adirondack-style Lodges feature rooms and suites with working fireplaces and terraces.

FACILITIES/SERVICES: Golf, tennis courts, spa, pool, private beach, fitness center, boating, children's programs and shops. Cross-country skiing, sledding and ice skating. Downhill skiing nearby.

BUSINESS SERVICES: Recently enhanced Business Center available.

DINING: "Trillium" for American Contemporary cuisine; the "Sagamore Dining Room" for Regional American and International selections; "Club Grill;" "Mister Brown's Pub" for casual dining; "The Morgan," a 19th-century touring vessel; "The Veranda" for afternoon tea, cocktails, tapas and sushi; and "The Pavillion" for lakeside seasonal lobster bakes.

MEETINGS: Total Meeting Rooms: 19 Total Sq. Ft.: 26,000 / Sq. M.: 2,421

RATES: USD 149.00 to 669.00; Corporate, Group, Package rates.

Mr. S. Lee Bowden,
Managing Director

110 Sagamore Road, P.O. Box 450
Bolton Landing, New York 12814, U.S.A.
Tel: +1.518.644.9400
Fax: +1.518.743.6036
Email: reserve@thesagamore.com
www.thesagamore.com

Worldwide Reservations

www.preferredhotels.com
800.323.7500 U.S.A./Canada
00.800.3237.5001 Europe (UIFN)
Other areas: *See page 192*

THE GARDEN CITY HOTEL

ACCOMMODATIONS: 280 total guestrooms, including 16 suites, each with two phones, data port, voice mail, newspaper, safe, mini-bar and robes. VCR on request.

FACILITIES/SERVICES: Fitness center, indoor swimming pool, Jacuzzi, sauna, concierge, valet parking, wireless Internet services, limousine service, dry cleaning, shoe shine, salon and gift shop.

BUSINESS SERVICES: On-site Business Center, secretarial and translating services, and notary public available. Courier service, fax services, office supplies.

DINING: "The Polo Restaurant" for contemporary American cuisine; "The Polo Lounge" for light snacks, cocktails and live entertainment; "Atrium Café" for homemade breads and pastries fresh-baked daily.

MEETINGS: Total Meeting Rooms: 16
Total Sq. Ft.: 25,000 / Sq. M.: 2,323

RATES: USD 275.00 to 2,150.00; Corporate, Group, Package rates.

Mr. Nasser Samman,
General Manager

45 Seventh Street
Garden City, New York 11530, U.S.A.
Tel: +1.516.747.3000
Fax: +1.516.747.1414
Email: info@gchotel.com
www.gardencityhotel.com

On the site where its famed predecessor was built in 1874, The Garden City Hotel offers the charm of the Old World combined with the conveniences of today. From its scenic village locale just outside New York City, guests experience the grandeur of the metropolitan area without the distractions of urban life. Garden City, on New York's Long Island, is a quaint village that boasts tree-lined streets, boutiques, trendy nightspots, restaurants and cafes. JFK Int'l. Airport: 12 miles/19 km, 16 minutes. La Guardia Airport: 16 miles/26 km, 22 minutes.

Worldwide Reservations
www.preferredhotels.com
800.323.7500 U.S.A./Canada
00.800.3237.5001 Europe (UIFN)
Other areas: See page 192

THE ST. REGIS NEW YORK

A 1904 Beaux Arts landmark, The St. Regis New York reigns as the flagship of The St. Regis brand. Situated along Fifth Avenue, this hotel offers a serene Midtown oasis with its Louis XVI decorated guest-rooms, high ceilings, silk wall coverings and spacious marble baths. Located near Central Park and Rockefeller Center, museums, galleries and theaters. John F. Kennedy Int'l. Airport: 17 miles/27 km; LaGuardia Airport: 10 miles/16 km; Newark Int'l. Airport: 18 miles/29 km.

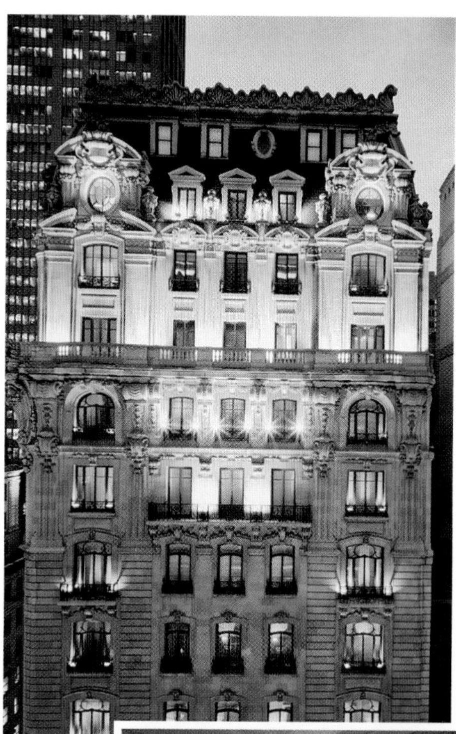

ACCOMMODATIONS: 222 total guestrooms, including 92 suites, each with multi-line phone, high-speed Internet access, voice mail, VCR, complimentary paper, fax machine, CD player, safe, mini-bar, robes and hair dryer.

FACILITIES/SERVICES: Spa, concierge services, 24-hour English-style butler service, shoe shine, fitness center, salon, dry cleaning, florist and shops. Complimentary tea/coffee service with wake-up call, fresh fruit and mineral water replenished daily.

BUSINESS SERVICES: On-site Business Center, secretarial and translating services available.

DINING: The hotel features "Lespinasse," a classic French restaurant; "Astor Court," which offers High Tea; and "King Cole Bar & Lounge."

MEETINGS: Total Meeting Rooms: 10 Total Sq. Ft.: 15,185 / Sq. M.: 1,414

RATES: USD 400.00 to 11,500.00; Corporate, Group, Package rates.

Mr. Guenter H. Richter, Managing Director

Two East 55th Street
New York, New York 10022, U.S.A.
Tel: +1.212.753.4500
Fax: +1.212.787.3447
Email: stregisny.res@stregis.com
www.stregis.com

Worldwide Reservations

www.preferredhotels.com
800.323.7500 U.S.A./Canada
00.800.3237.5001 Europe (UIFN)
Other areas: See page 192

BALLANTYNE RESORT

ACCOMMODATIONS: 214 total guestrooms, including 22 suites, each with two multi-line phones, voice mail & data port, robes, hair dryer, iron/board, newspaper and safe. VCR available on request.

FACILITIES/SERVICES: 18-hole, par-71 golf course, tennis courts, spa, concierge services, shoe shine, fitness center, salon, tennis, dry cleaning and shops.

BUSINESS SERVICES: On-site Business Center and secretarial services available.

DINING: With sweeping views of the 18th fairway, "The Grill Room" offers extravagant daily breakfasts and luncheon buffets. For dinner, the warmth and intimate "Club Room" offers à la carte specialties with an international flair.

MEETINGS: Total Meeting Rooms: 22
Total Sq. Ft.: 16,000 / Sq. M.: 1,490

RATES: USD 180.00 to 895.00; Corporate, Group, Package rates.

Mr. Steve Brooks, Director of Sales

10000 Ballantyne Commons Parkway
Charlotte, North Carolina 28134,
U.S.A.
Tel: +1.704.248.4000
Fax: +1.704.248.4005
Email:
reservations@ballantyneresort.com
www.ballantyneresort.com

Ballantyne Resort signals the return of the "Grand Hotel." Nestled in the gently rolling hills of North Carolina, Ballantyne Resort welcomes guests to a world of elegant architecture, gracious service and uncompromising quality in a true resort setting. Prominently set in Ballantyne, Charlotte's premier neighborhood, the resort is within walking distance of shops and restaurants. Charlotte/Douglas Int'l. Airport: 12 miles/20 km, 20 minutes.

Worldwide Reservations
www.preferredhotels.com
800.323.7500 U.S.A./Canada
00.800.3237.5001 Europe (UIFN)
Other areas: See page 192

THE PARK HOTEL

Traditional architecture, period furnishings and a large art collection make The Park Hotel a cozy retreat or a comfortable headquarters for business. Nestled in the South Park neighborhood, the hotel is surrounded by upscale shops, restaurants and boutiques. The hotel features a warm and friendly staff as well as intimate and elegant furnishings. Located within 20 minutes of the theater district, performing arts venues and uptown business district. Charlotte/Douglas Int'l. Airport: 10 miles/ 16 km, 20 minutes.

ACCOMMODATIONS: 192 total guestrooms, including 8 suites, each with two phones, data port, voice mail, safe, high-speed Internet access and robes. VCR available on request.

FACILITIES/SERVICES: Health club, concierge, shoe shine and nearby golf at Ballantyne Golf Club.

BUSINESS SERVICES: On-site Business Center.

DINING: Enjoy a varietal menu at "Smoky's Grill" in a relaxed and comfortable atmosphere, or cocktails in the adjoining bar, richly appointed in mahogany and leather.

MEETINGS: Total Meeting Rooms: 10 Total Sq. Ft.: 8,102 / Sq. M.: 754

RATES: USD 139.00 to 1,200.00; Group, Package rates.

Mr. Michael P. Zubel,
General Manager

2200 Rexford Road
Charlotte, North Carolina 28211,
U.S.A.
Tel: +1.704.364.8220
Fax: +1.704.365.4712
Email: reserve@theparkhotel.com
www.theparkhotel.com

Worldwide Reservations
www.preferredhotels.com
800.323.7500 U.S.A./Canada
00.800.3237.5001 Europe (UIFN)
Other areas: See page 192

THE CINCINNATIAN HOTEL

Built in 1882, The Cincinnatian Hotel is complemented by European décor, traditional architecture and a large art collection. Nestled downtown, the hotel is in the heart of upscale shops, restaurants and boutiques. Unforgettable accommodations, memorable dining and stellar service combine to make this hotel a cozy retreat or a comfortable headquarters for business. Located at Sixth and Vine streets, one block from Fountain Square near the Aronoff Center for the Arts, the Convention Center, sports stadiums. Greater Cincinnati/N. Kentucky Int'l. Airport: 13 miles/21 km, 20 minutes.

ACCOMMODATIONS: 146 total guestrooms, including 8 suites, each with two multi-line phones, data port, voice mail in four languages, high-speed Internet access, newspaper, safe, mini-bar, hair dryer and robes. VCR on request.

FACILITIES/SERVICES: Garden bath, whirlpool, or electric fireplace available, fitness center, concierge, child care services, dry cleaning, shoe shine and florist.

BUSINESS SERVICES: Secretarial services available.

DINING: Dine on Regional American Cuisine in the elegant "Palace Restaurant," then relax in "The Cricket Lounge" with a nightcap.

MEETINGS: Total Meeting Rooms: 6
Total Sq. Ft.: 3,157 / Sq. M.: 294

RATES: USD 225.00 to 1,500.00; Corporate, Group, Package rates.

Mrs. Denise Vandersall,
Managing Director

601 Vine Street
Cincinnati, Ohio 45202, U.S.A.
Tel: +1.513.381.3000
Fax: +1.513.651.0256
Email: info@cincinnatianhotel.com
www.cincinnatianhotel.com

Worldwide Reservations
www.preferredhotels.com
800.323.7500 U.S.A./Canada
00.800.3237.5001 Europe (UIFN)
Other areas: See page 192

THE HEATHMAN HOTEL

Built in 1927, The Heathman is an artistic masterpiece, a timeless classic offering attentive service by a "Personal Concierge." Recognized as one of the "Top 100 Hotels" in the US and Canada by *Travel & Leisure* magazine. Guests can lose themselves in the original art throughout the hotel or revel in the sounds of jazz in the signature "Tea Court." In the heart of downtown Portland's Cultural District and next to the Portland Center for Performing Arts. Portland Int'l. Airport: 9 miles/15 km, 20 minutes.

ACCOMMODATIONS: 150 total guestrooms, including 33 suites, each with two multi-line phones, data port, high-speed Internet access, voice mail, newspaper, French-press coffee, CD alarm clock radio, hair dryer, mini-bar, robes and access to a 400-title complimentary movie library.

FACILITIES/SERVICES: Fitness center, concierge, tea service, slippers with turndown and dry cleaning.

BUSINESS SERVICES: Secretarial, translating services and work station with color printer, scanner and fax.

DINING: The James Beard award-winning "Heathman Restaurant" features French cuisine with Pacific Northwest ingredients.

MEETINGS: Total Meeting Rooms: 8 Total Sq. Ft.: 3,495 / Sq. M.: 325

RATES: USD 150.00 to 750.00; Corporate, Group, Package rates.

Mr. Jeff Jobe, General Manager

1001 S.W. Broadway
Portland, Oregon 97205, U.S.A.
Tel: +1.503.241.4100
Fax: +1.503.790.7110
Email: info@heathmanhotel.com
www.heathmanhotel.com

Worldwide Reservations
www.preferredhotels.com
800.323.7500 U.S.A./Canada
00.800.3237.5001 Europe (UIFN)
Other areas: See page 192

FROM HEAD TO TOE, THE PREFERRED SPA EXPERIENCE IS THE ULTIMATE INDULGENCE

FROM A SOOTHING HOT ROCK MASSAGE to a sensuous chocolate bath, rejuvenate and luxuriate with unique spa experiences at Preferred Hotels & Resorts. The spa at **Anassa**, an inviting resort on the isle of Cyprus with breathtaking views of the Mediterranean, offers a unique history lesson with its centuries-old thalassotherapy treatments. At **Bacara Resort & Spa**, nestled on 78 acres (32 hectares) of pristine beachfront between the Pacific Ocean and the Santa Ynez Mountains, experience the ultimate in serenity and luxury at the 42,000-square-foot (3,910-square-meter) spa, featuring 35 treatment rooms, an outdoor spa pool and a cafe with healthy fare. For a rejuvenating urban spa experience in the heart of San Francisco, visit the Nob Hill Spa & Wellness Center at the Huntington Hotel. An exquisite full-service European spa awaits guests of **Topnotch at Stowe Resort & Spa**, a 1,200 acre (49-hectare) resort nestled at the foot of Vermont's highest peak, Mount Mansfield. And what chocolate lover could resist the tempting menu of luscious chocolate treatments and wraps at **The Hotel Hershey®**?

For more information on a Preferred spa experience, refer to page 192 for a local reservation number or visit our Web site at www.preferredhotels.com.

THE HOTEL HERSHEY®

ACCOMMODATIONS: 234 total guestrooms, including 25 suites, each with three multi-line phones, data port, voice mail, CD player, newspaper, hair dryers and robes. VCR on request.

FACILITIES/SERVICES: Spa, fitness center, tennis, indoor/outdoor pools, bocce court, basketball and volleyball courts, carriage rides, jogging trails, championship golf and concierge.

BUSINESS SERVICES: Business Center and secretarial service.

DINING: Contemporary American cuisine in the award-winning "Circular Dining Room," casual dining in "The Fountain Cafe," seasonal fare at the "Club House Cafe & Creamery," or cocktails and light fare at the "Iberian Lounge." Pastry and coffee shop are also available.

MEETINGS: Total Meeting Rooms: 20
Total Sq. Ft.: 22,000 / Sq. M.: 2,048

RATES: USD 189.00 to 2,500.00; Corporate, Group, Package rates.

Mr. Stephen Bello, General Manager

Hotel Road
Hershey, Pennsylvania 17033, U.S.A.
Tel: +1.717.533.2171
Fax: +1.717.534.8887
Email: info@hersheypa.com
www.hersheypa.com

THE HOTEL HERSHEY offers a mix of European splendor set amid the picturesque countryside and is reminiscent of the dreams of its founder, Chocolate King Milton S. Hershey. Styled after a 19th-century Mediterranean resort, the hotel offers state-of-the-art amenities, including The Spa at THE HOTEL HERSHEY, along with the charm of restored balustrades, original mosaic tiles and hand-sculpted fountains. Close to Pennsylvania Dutch Country, Gettysburg and HERSHEYPARK®. Harrisburg Int'l. Airport: 15 miles/24 km, 15 minutes.

Worldwide Reservations
www.preferredhotels.com
800.323.7500 U.S.A./Canada
00.800.3237.5001 Europe (UIFN)
Other areas: See page 192

THE RITTENHOUSE HOTEL

An intimate oasis on Rittenhouse Square, where guests arrive to a Belgian stone courtyard, a fountain and manicured gardens. The marble foyer leads to the hotel's lobby, appointed with traditional furnishings and a warm ambiance. Downtown Philadelphia, adjacent to the business district, premier shopping and restaurants. Five minutes from the train station and historic sites. Philadelphia Int'l. Airport: 8 miles/13 km, 20 minutes.

ACCOMMODATIONS: 98 total guestrooms, including 11 suites, each with three multi-line speaker phones, data port, voice mail, fax machine, VCR, CD player, newspaper, robes, hair dryer, mini-bar and luxurious bathrooms with marble shower, tub and mini-televisions.

FACILITIES/SERVICES: Spa, health club, tennis courts (off-site), concierge, child care services, dry cleaning, salon, indoor pool and outdoor sundeck.

BUSINESS SERVICES: Business Center, secretarial services, translating services and travel agent.

DINING: Innovative cuisine at "Lacroix at the Rittenhouse," prime steak and seafood at "Smith & Wollensky," light fare at "Boathouse Row Bar," traditional British tea at "Cassatt Tea Room."

MEETINGS: Total Meeting Rooms: 6
Total Sq. Ft.: 8,470 / Sq. M.: 787

RATES: USD 345.00 to 1,800.00; Corporate, Group, Package rates.

Mr. David G. Benton,
Vice President & General Manager

---

210 West Rittenhouse Square
Philadelphia, Pennsylvania 19103, U.S.A.
Tel: +1.215.546.9000
Fax: +1.215.732.3364
Email: ktruman@rittenhousehotel.com
www.rittenhousehotel.com

Worldwide Reservations
www.preferredhotels.com
800.323.7500 U.S.A./Canada
00.800.3237.5001 Europe (UIFN)
Other areas: *See page 192*

CHARLESTON PLACE

ACCOMMODATIONS: 442 total guestrooms, including 42 suites, all featuring period furnishings, Southern-style armoires, distinctive baths with Botticino marble, cable TV/VCR, direct-dial phone with messaging and data port capabilities.

FACILITIES/SERVICES: Spa, indoor/outdoor swimming pool, state-of-the-art health club, rooftop tennis courts, concierge, child care services, dry cleaning, shoe shine and shops.

BUSINESS SERVICES: Business Center, secretarial and translating services.

DINING: "Charleston Grill," winner of the Mobil Travel Four Star Award, features traditional Low Country cuisine with Continental flair; "Palmetto Café" features contemporary modern cuisine; "The Lobby Lounge" offers fabulous afternoon tea, cocktails and piano accompaniment.

MEETINGS: Total Meeting Rooms: 25 Total Sq. Ft.: 33,000 / Sq. M.: 3,072

RATES: USD 215.00 to 1,500.00; Corporate, Group, Package rates.

Mr. Paul M. Stracey, General Manager

205 Meeting Street
Charleston, South Carolina 29401, U.S.A.
Tel: +1.843.722.4900
Fax: +1.843.722.0728
Email: achavez@orientx.net
www.charlestonplacehotel.com

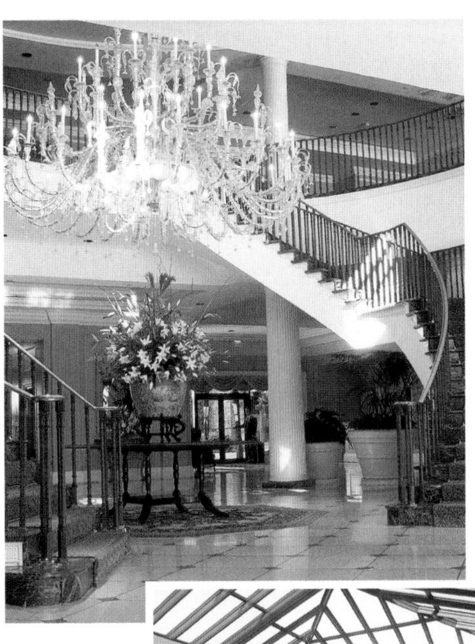

Known for its signature double staircase and 12-foot chandelier in the Italian-marbled lobby, Charleston Place offers unparalleled accommodations in the heart of the Historic District. Guests of this traditional hotel are enchanted by the refined furnishings, embraced by the grand open-armed staircase and entertained with the finest in Southern hospitality.

In downtown Historic Charleston within walking distance of upscale shopping and award-winning dining.

Charleston Int'l. Airport: 10 miles/16 km, 25 minutes.

Worldwide Reservations
www.preferredhotels.com
800.323.7500 U.S.A./Canada
00.800.3237.5001 Europe (UIFN)
Other areas: See page 192

THE PEABODY MEMPHIS

ACCOMMODATIONS: 468 total guestrooms, including 15 suites, each with multi-line phones, data port, voice mail and newspaper. VCR on request. Some rooms with robes.

FACILITIES/SERVICES: Pool, fitness center, massage, sauna, steam room, whirlpool, aerobics, dry cleaning, shoe shine, salon and shops.

BUSINESS SERVICES: Business Center available.

DINING: Choose "Chez Philippe," the only Four Star-rated restaurant in the Mid-South region, for classic French cuisine and "Capriccio" for Northern Italian cuisine. 24-hour in-room dining.

MEETINGS: Total Meeting Rooms: 35
Total Sq. Ft.: 80,000 / Sq. M.: 7,448

RATES: USD 195.00 to 1,675.00; Corporate, Group, Package rates.

Mr. Victor Mills, General Manager

---

149 Union Avenue
Memphis, Tennessee 38103, U.S.A.
Tel: +1.901.529.4000
Fax: +1.901.529.3600
Email: pmreservations@peabodymemphis.com
www.peabodymemphis.com

Known as the South's Grand Hotel and built in 1925 in Italian Renaissance style, The Peabody features a magnificent Grand Lobby, high tea and the famous Peabody Marching Ducks. In the downtown Memphis business district, adjacent to Peabody Place Entertainment & Retail Complex Center. Walking distance to Memphis Cook Convention Center, two blocks to Beale Street — "Home of the Blues," and a short drive to Graceland, The National Civil Rights Museum and other attractions. Memphis Int'l. Airport: 12 miles/19 km, 15 minutes.

Worldwide Reservations
www.preferredhotels.com
800.323.7500 U.S.A./Canada
00.800.3237.5001 Europe (UIFN)
Other areas: See page 192

Opening February 2003

THE HERMITAGE HOTEL

Recently renovated, this luxurious historic hotel is one of Nashville's only remaining commercial Beaux Arts structures. Centrally located downtown, adjacent to the State Capitol Building and within walking distance of all major business and entertainment venues, The Hermitage Hotel offers a warm and elegant sanctuary within the city, as well as the finest accommodations and service in all of Nashville. Nashville Int'l. Airport: 10 miles/16 km, 15 minutes.

ACCOMMODATIONS: 123 total guestrooms, including 4 suites, each luxurious and oversized room features down-filled duvets, designer soaps, marble bathrooms, three multi-line phones, data port, newspaper, CD/DVD player, safe, mini-bar, robes and hair dryer.

FACILITIES/SERVICES: Concierge service, shoe shine, laundry/dry cleaning service, sundries shop. Fitness center features strength equipment, as well as TVs on elliptical machines, bikes and treadmills. Massage therapy rooms with lockers and showers.

BUSINESS SERVICES: Business Services, secretarial and translating services.

DINING: The renowned "Capitol Grille Restaurant," serves all meals and features evening entertainment and Nashville's best Sunday Brunch. "The Oak Bar" has been meticulously restored and is a favorite retreat.

MEETINGS: Total Meeting Rooms: 5 Total Sq. Ft.: 5,271 / Sq. M.: 491

RATES: USD 195.00 to 1,500.00; Corporate, Group, Package rates.

Mr. Greg Sligh, General Manager

---

231 Sixth Avenue North
Nashville, Tennessee 37219, U.S.A.
Tel: +1.615.244.3121
Fax: +1.615.254.6909
Email: reservations@thehermitagehotel.com
www.thehermitagehotel.com

Worldwide Reservations

www.preferredhotels.com

800.323.7500 U.S.A./Canada

00.800.3237.5001 Europe (UIFN)

Other areas: See page 192

HOTEL DEREK

With its crisp, tailored look, custom-designed furnishings, original artwork and contemporary pieces, Hotel Derek creates a bold new statement and international style, simultaneously celebrating its Texas heritage. Hotel Derek reflects all the energy and sophistication the city has to offer. Located in Uptown Houston, a short walk from the Galleria and convenient to downtown and the Texas Medical Center. Bush Intercontinental Airport: 25 miles/41 km, 35 minutes. Hobby Airport: 15 miles, 24 km, 25 minutes.

ACCOMMODATIONS: 314 total guestrooms, including 10 suites, each with two dual-line cordless phones, voice mail, data port, Internet access, CD clock radio, VCR on request, newspaper, safe and mini-bar. Fax machine available in some rooms and Internet access via TV.

FACILITIES/SERVICES: Concierge, child care services, shoe shine, dry cleaning, evening turndown service and valet parking for all guests. Fitness center with spa treatment suite.

BUSINESS SERVICES: Business Center, secretarial services and 16 studio rooms with business alcoves offering a fax/copier/printer, television.

DINING: "Maverick" restaurant serves spicy regional and Southwestern cuisine in a warm, gallery-like setting. The bar and lobby lounge have intimate alcoves for cocktails.

MEETINGS: Total Meeting Rooms: 9
Total Sq. Ft.: 10,250 / Sq. M.: 954

RATES: USD 245.00 to 875.00; Corporate, Group, Package rates.

Mr. David M. Hill, General Manager

2525 West Loop South
Houston, Texas 77027, U.S.A.
Tel: +1.713.961.3000
Fax: +1.713.297.4392
Email: derek@hotelderek.com
www.hotelderek.com

Worldwide Reservations
www.preferredhotels.com
800.323.7500 U.S.A./Canada
00.800.3237.5001 Europe (UIFN)
Other areas: See page 192

THE HOUSTONIAN HOTEL, CLUB & SPA

In the tradition of a grand Texas lodge, The Houstonian blends modern comforts with Old World charm. Nestled on 18 wooded acres (7 hectares) of towering pines and majestic oaks in the heart of the Galleria, the hotel extends expressions of Texas warmth and hospitality to every detail. Located in uptown Houston and convenient to downtown and Memorial Park. Bush Int'l. Airport: 22 miles/35 km, 30 minutes.

ACCOMMODATIONS: 288 total guestrooms, including 9 suites, each with two multi-line cordless phones, data port, voice mail, mini-bar and safe. VCR on request.

FACILITIES/SERVICES: Nationally recognized Houstonian Club offers 100 group exercise classes each week, 200 exercise machines, tennis, paddleball, racquetball, squash courts, rock climbing wall, running tracks, pools and a children's gymnasium. Concierge, child care services and shops also available. New spa offers the most current treatments available.

BUSINESS SERVICES: Business Center, secretarial service and in-room computers with Internet access.

DINING: "Olivette" combines ancient culinary traditions of the Mediterranean with American touches. "The Manor House" features superb cuisine, gorgeous views and a refined atmosphere.

MEETINGS: Total Meeting Rooms: 26
Total Sq. Ft.: 33,000 / Sq. M.: 3,072

RATES: USD 295.00 to 1,800.00; Corporate, Group, Package rates.

Mr. Mark S. Yanke,
V.P. & Managing Director

111 North Post Oak Lane
Houston, Texas 77024, U.S.A.
Tel: +1.713.680.2626
Fax: +1.713.680.2992
Email: sales1@houstonian.com
www.houstonian.com

Worldwide Reservations
www.preferredhotels.com
800.323.7500 U.S.A./Canada
00.800.3237.5001 Europe (UIFN)
Other areas: See page 192

LA MANSIÓN DEL RIO

Situated along the romantic San Antonio River Walk, this Spanish Colonial mansion recently completed a $15-million renovation under the direction of nationally acclaimed designer Trish Wilson and Associates. An intimate hotel where Old World charm mingles with the excitement and energy of an international city. Downtown on the San Antonio River Walk, within easy walking distance of the Alamo, the convention center and other attractions. San Antonio Int'l. Airport: 12 miles/19 km, 20 minutes.

ACCOMMODATIONS: 337 total guestrooms, including 11 suites, each with three multi-line phones, data port, voice mail, mini-bar, robes, Web TV, hair dryers, iron & board, and coffee maker. VCR on request.

FACILITIES/SERVICES: Heated pool, fitness center, concierge, child care services, dry cleaning, shoe shine.

BUSINESS SERVICES: On-site Business Center and secretarial services available.

DINING: "Las Canarias" is an award-winning culinary destination located on the romantic River Walk. Enjoy new American cuisine with regional influences prepared by nationally recognized chef Scott Cohen. 24-hour in-room dining also available.

MEETINGS: Total Meeting Rooms: 14
Total Sq. Ft.: 15,000 / Sq. M.: 1,396

RATES: USD 199.00 to 1,900.00; Corporate, Group, Package rates.

Mr. Michael Bazar, General Manager

112 College Street
San Antonio, Texas 78205, U.S.A.
Tel: +1.210.518.1000
Fax: +1.210.226.0389
Email: lmdr@lamansion.com
www.lamansion.com

Worldwide Reservations
www.preferredhotels.com
800.323.7500 U.S.A./Canada
00.800.3237.5001 Europe (UIFN)
Other areas: *See page 192*

STEIN ERIKSEN LODGE

ACCOMMODATIONS: 170 total guestrooms, including 59 suites, each with multi-line phones, data port, voice mail, Internet access, CD player, complimentary newspaper, safe, mini-bar, robes, hair dryer and bottled water. VCR & DVD are available upon request.

FACILITIES/SERVICES: Snow skiing, pool, spa, snowmobiling, cross-country skiing, mountain biking, hiking, golf, tennis, hot air ballooning, fitness center, child care services and concierge.

BUSINESS SERVICES: Business Center and secretarial services.

DINING: "The Giltretind Restaurant" features an extensive wine list and gourmet cuisine in a warm, elegant setting.

MEETINGS: Total Meeting Rooms: 7
Total Sq. Ft.: 5,500 / Sq. M.: 512

RATES: USD 195.00 to 3,000.00; Group, Package rates.

Mr. Russ Olsen, General Manager

7700 Stein Way, P.O. Box 3177
Park City, Utah 84060, U.S.A.
Tel: +1.435.649.3700
Fax: +1.435.649.5825
Email: info@steinlodge.com
www.steinlodge.com

This European-style lodge exudes rustic Norwegian elegance and Old World charm with its beamed cathedral ceilings and great stone fireplaces. Nestled amid aspens and pines, high in the Rocky Mountains, the lodge is a blend of Alpine splendor with refined accommodations and attentive service. Located in Silver Lake Village, mid-mountain at Deer Valley Resort. Salt Lake City Int'l. Airport: 38 miles/61 km, 45 minutes.

Worldwide Reservations
www.preferredhotels.com
800.323.7500 U.S.A./Canada
00.800.3237.5001 Europe (UIFN)
Other areas: See page 192

TOPNOTCH AT STOWE RESORT & SPA

Natural woods and earth tones complement the contemporary design of this resort, which is nestled at the foot of Vermont's highest peak, Mount Mansfield, on 120 spectacular acres (49 hectares) of New England countryside. Topnotch at Stowe Resort & Spa offers the perfect balance of scenery, unrivaled accommodations, amenities and some of the most exquisite cuisine in the Northeast. In the Green Mountains, four miles from the historic village of Stowe and 1.5 miles from the ski slopes. Burlington Int'l. Airport: 35 miles/56 km, 40 minutes.

ACCOMMODATIONS: 90 total guestrooms, including 13 suites, and 22 townhomes, each with voice mail, data port, in-room movies, newspaper, mini-refrigerator, robes, iron & board, safe, hair dryer and coffee maker.

FACILITIES/SERVICES: Tennis courts, pools, fitness center, whirlpool, sauna, equestrian center, biking trails, cross-country and downhill skiing, spa and salon.

BUSINESS SERVICES: Business Center and secretarial services.

DINING: Topnotch's award-winning chef creates gourmet cuisine in the main dining room, "Maxwell's at Topnotch." "The Buttertub Bistro and Lounge" offers nightly entertainment and light fare.

MEETINGS: Total Meeting Rooms: 6 Total Sq. Ft.: 10,000 / Sq. M.: 931

RATES: USD 250.00 to 750.00; Corporate, Group, Package rates.

Mr. Reggie Cooper,
President & General Manager

4000 Mountain Road
Stowe, Vermont 05672, U.S.A.
Tel: +1.802.253.8585
Fax: +1.802.253.9263
Email: info@topnotchresort.com
www.topnotch-resort.com

Worldwide Reservations
www.preferredhotels.com
800.323.7500 U.S.A./Canada
00.800.3237.5001 Europe (UIFN)
Other areas: *See page 192*

KESWICK HALL AT MONTICELLO

ACCOMMODATIONS: 48 total guestrooms, including 3 suites, each with two multi-line phones, data port, voice mail, VCR, robes and hair dryer.

FACILITIES/SERVICES: 18-hole Arnold Palmer golf course, indoor/outdoor pools, croquet lawn, mountain bikes, hot air ballooning, spa, fitness center, concierge services, shoe shine, child care services, floodlit tennis, horseback riding and florist.

BUSINESS SERVICES: Secretarial and translating services. Copier and computer available.

DINING: The restaurant offers stunning views over the estate, romantic outside dining and regional American cuisine. "Palmer Room" offers traditional club dining, "The Club Bar" serves cocktails and lighter meals. Traditional afternoon tea served daily.

MEETINGS: Total Meeting Rooms: 6
Total Sq. Ft.: 7,970 / Sq. M.: 742

RATES: USD 295.00 to 685.00; Corporate, Group, Package rates.

Mr. Michael Pownall,
General Manager

701 Club Drive
Keswick, Virginia 22947, U.S.A.
Tel: +1.434.979.3440
Fax: +1.434.977.4171
Email: keswick@keswick.com
www.keswick.com

Keswick Hall combines the enchantment of a country estate with elements of a Tuscan-style villa. Nestled over 600 acres (243 hectares) of emerald-green fairways and European gardens, and complemented by artwork and antiques, this resort offers a warm, magical atmosphere. Located five miles from downtown Charlottesville and minutes from Jefferson's Monticello. At the foot of the Blue Ridge Mountains, Charlottesville is 64 miles west of Richmond. Charlottesville Airport: 12 miles/19 km, 20 minutes.

Worldwide Reservations
www.preferredhotels.com
800.323.7500 U.S.A./Canada
00.800.3237.5001 Europe (UIFN)
Other areas: See page 192

THE JEFFERSON HOTEL

Nestled in the heart of Richmond's charming downtown historic district and built in 1895, this Beaux Arts hotel is renowned for its breathtaking public spaces, luxurious accommodations and unsurpassed genuine and gracious service. A memorable experience awaits every guest. Just blocks from the financial district, the hotel is centrally located within downtown for convenient access to shopping, dining and entertainment. Richmond Int'l. Airport: 9 miles/16 km, 15 minutes.

ACCOMMODATIONS: 264 total guestrooms, including 37 suites, each with three multi-line phones, data port, voice mail, complimentary newspaper, CD player, safe, mini-bar, hair dryer and robes. VCR available on request.

FACILITIES/SERVICES: Indoor pool, fitness center with free weights, concierge, babysitting, dry cleaning, complimentary downtown transportation, salon, florist and shops.

BUSINESS SERVICES: On-site Business Center, secretarial and translating services available.

DINING: "Lemaire" featuring French cuisine with a Southern flair and "TJ's Restaurant and Lounge" for less formal dining. 24-hour in-room dining also available.

MEETINGS: Total Meeting Rooms: 18 Total Sq. Ft.: 26,000 / Sq. M.: 2,421

RATES: USD 285.00 to 1,800.00; Corporate, Group, Package rates.

Mr. Joseph Longo, General Manager

101 West Franklin Street
Richmond, Virginia 23220, U.S.A.
Tel: +1.804.788.8000
Fax: +1.804.225.0334
Email: jefferson.sales@jefferson-hotel.com
www.jefferson-hotel.com

Worldwide Reservations

www.preferredhotels.com
800.323.7500 U.S.A./Canada
00.800.3237.5001 Europe (UIFN)
Other areas: *See page 192*

KINGSMILL RESORT

ACCOMMODATIONS: 400 total guestrooms, including 185 suites, with all villa-style guestrooms and suites offering river, golf and tennis views. Some feature full kitchens and living rooms with fireplaces.

FACILITIES/SERVICES: 63 holes of golf, The Spa at Kingsmill, 15 tennis courts, Sports Club, two pools, ball courts, fitness center, marina and seasonal children's program.

BUSINESS SERVICES: Conference concierge for each meeting, continuous break service and on-site Business Center with T-1 Internet access.

DINING: Five restaurants and lounges, including "Eagles," an authentic steak and chop house featuring Kingsmill's exclusive beechwood-smoked cooking and an extensive selection of fine wines.

MEETINGS: Total Meeting Rooms: 16
Total Sq. Ft.: 16,000 / Sq. M.: 1,490

RATES: USD 129.00 to 937.00; Group, Package rates.

Mr. Joseph Durante III, Executive Vice President & Managing Director

1010 Kingsmill Road
Williamsburg, Virginia 23185, U.S.A.
Tel: +1.757.253.1703
Fax: +1.757.253.8237
Email: reservations@kingsmill.com
www.kingsmill.com

Contemporary architecture and furnishings welcome guests to this immaculately landscaped setting situated along Virginia's historic James River. Water views provide a relaxing backdrop to golf, tennis and other resort activities. Set on 3,000 acres (1,214 hectares) of woodlands overlooking the James River in Williamsburg, Virginia. Williamsburg/Newport News Int'l. Airport: 12 miles/19 km, 20 minutes.

Worldwide Reservations
www.preferredhotels.com
800.323.7500 U.S.A./Canada
00.800.3237.5001 Europe (UIFN)
Other areas: See page 192

SEMIAHMOO RESORT

Nestled on a waterfront wildlife preserve, Semiahmoo Resort, surrounded by water on three sides, offers an endless stretch of beach, views of the Canadian Gulf Islands and acres of wooded trails. Guests enjoy gracious service, views of snow-capped mountains, and a variety of outdoor activities. Situated along the Puget Sound coastline near the San Juan Islands and Cascade Mountains. Convenient to ferry and train systems. Sea-Tac Int'l. Airport: 150 miles/241 km, 2 hours. Vancouver Int'l. Airport: 40 miles/64 km, 45 minutes.

ACCOMMODATIONS: 198 total guestrooms, including 28 suites, each with two multi-line phones, data port and voice mail.

FACILITIES/SERVICES: Two championship golf courses, sailboat charters, kayaking, spa and salon, fitness center, tennis, pool, concierge, dry cleaning, cafe, shops and free concert series.

BUSINESS SERVICES: 24-hour Business Center available.

DINING: Restaurants feature spectacular views and regional cuisine and include a waterfront restaurant, pub and golf course dining.

MEETINGS: Total Meeting Rooms: 16 Total Sq. Ft.: 22,000 / Sq. M.: 2,048

RATES: USD 99.00 to 399.00; Corporate, Group, Package rates.

Mr. Tom Waithe, Managing Director

9565 Semiahmoo Parkway
Blaine, Washington 98230, U.S.A.
Tel: +1.360.318.2000
Fax: +1.360.318.2087
Email: info@semiahmoo.com
www.semiahmoo.com

Worldwide Reservations
www.preferredhotels.com
800.323.7500 U.S.A./Canada
00.800.3237.5001 Europe (UIFN)
Other areas: *See page 192*

SORRENTO HOTEL

ACCOMMODATIONS: 76 total guestrooms, including 42 suites, each with data port, voice mail, stereos with CD players, robes, mini-bar, high-speed Internet access, cordless phones, 400-thread count linens and pillow-top mattresses.

FACILITIES/SERVICES: Nautilus exercise center, babysitting, dry cleaning, shoe shine, salon, town car service and concierge.

BUSINESS SERVICES: Business Center and complimentary high-speed Internet access.

DINING: "Hunt Club" serves regional Northwest and Mediterranean cuisine. "Fireside Room" features cocktails, light menu and entertainment. "Piazza Capri" offers seasonal dining alfresco.

MEETINGS: Total Meeting Rooms: 4
Total Sq. Ft.: 4,000 / Sq. M.: 372

RATES: USD 250.00 to 2,500.00; Corporate, Group, Package rates.

Mr. Stan Kott, Vice President and General Manager

---

900 Madison Street
Seattle, Washington 98104, U.S.A.
Tel: +1.206.622.6400
Fax: +1.206.343.6155
Email: mail@hotelsorrento.com
www.hotelsorrento.com

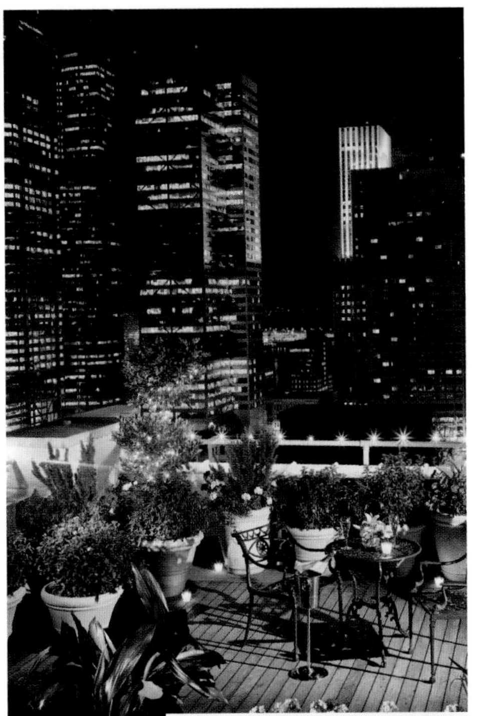

Gracing the city with its breathtaking Italianate architecture for nearly a century, the Sorrento is a stylish oasis and one of Seattle's most recognizable and cherished landmarks. Overlooking the downtown skyline, Puget Sound and the Olympic Mountains, the hotel offers rich decor, casual elegance and Mediterranean-inspired cuisine and ambiance. Convenient to financial, medical and shopping districts. Seattle-Tacoma Int'l. Airport: 14 miles/ 23 km, 25 minutes.

Worldwide Reservations
www.preferredhotels.com
800.323.7500 U.S.A./Canada
00.800.3237.5001 Europe (UIFN)
Other areas: See page 192

THE WOODMARK HOTEL ON LAKE WASHINGTON

The luxury of this lakeside retreat and world-class spa embraces travelers with the charm of a private residence. Combining intimacy and elegance, The Woodmark showcases shoreline views of the Seattle skyline and Olympic Mountains, and is the only hotel located on the shores of Lake Washingon, 20 minutes east of Seattle. Prominently set within a waterfront community, minutes from shopping, galleries, the high-tech corridors of Redmond/ Bellevue, and tourist destinations. Seattle-Tacoma Int'l. Airport: 18 miles/30 km, 30 minutes.

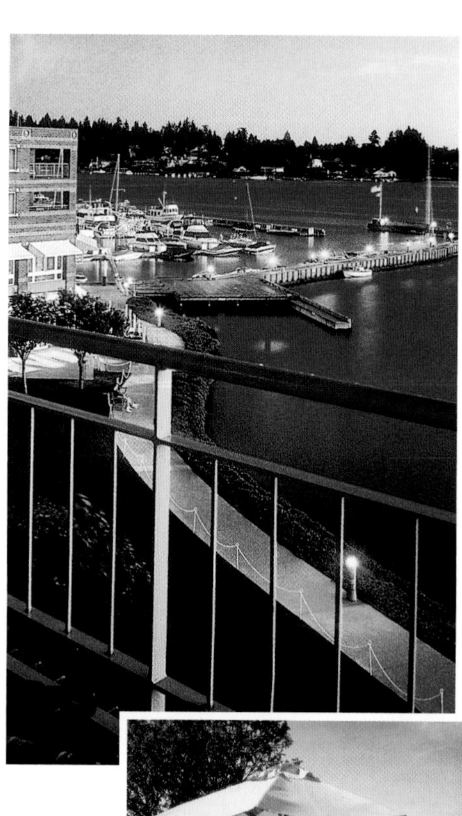

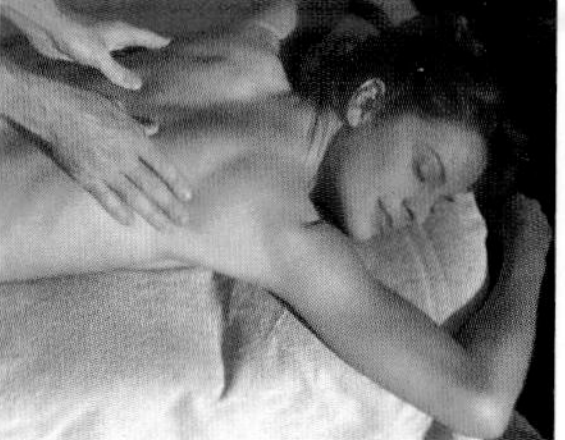

ACCOMMODATIONS: 100 total guestrooms, including 21 suites, each with Internet access, voice mail, data port, newspaper, CD player, safe, robes, hair dryer and mini-bar. Many with balcony and lake views.

FACILITIES/SERVICES: Spa treatments, plush bedding and pillow selection. Concierge, shoe shine, child care services, salon, dry cleaning, shops and travel agency. Complimentary amenities: Internet access, late-night snacks and fitness center.

BUSINESS SERVICES: Airline ticketing, secretarial and translating services.

DINING: "Waters Lakeside Bistro" for Northwest cuisine, "Cucina Carillon Point" for Italian, "Yarrow Bay Beach Café & Grill" for seafood and "The Library Bar" for afternoon tea and libations.

MEETINGS: Total Meeting Rooms: 7 Total Sq. Ft.: 4,936 / Sq. M.: 460

RATES: USD 205.00 to 1,800.00; Corporate, Group, Package rates.

Mr. Marc Nowak, General Manager

1200 Carillon Point
Kirkland, Washington 98033, U.S.A.
Tel: +1.425.822.3700
Fax: +1.425.822.3699
Email: mail@thewoodmark.com
www.thewoodmark.com

Worldwide Reservations

www.preferredhotels.com
800.323.7500 U.S.A./Canada
00.800.3237.5001 Europe (UIFN)
Other areas: See page 192

WILLOWS LODGE

Rural and rustic in ambiance, Willows Lodge is one of the latest entries into greater Seattle's collection of luxury lodgings and spas. This 86-room, Northwest-style lodge is situated in Woodinville on five exquisitely landscaped acres (2 hectares) that border the Sammamish River in the heart of Cascade wine country. Adjacent to Chateau Ste. Michelle and Columbia Wineries, Redhook Brewery and close to the Silicon Forest of the Pacific Northwest. Seattle-Tacoma Int'l. Airport: 35 miles/56 km, 45 minutes.

ACCOMMODATIONS: 86 total guestrooms, including 6 suites, most with garden views. Extensive woodwork, stone fireplaces, quality beds with down duvets and linens by Frette, CD/DVD systems, patios, multi-line cordless phones, customized mini-bar, complimentary high-speed Internet access, voice mail and robes.

FACILITIES/SERVICES: The spa pampers you with massage, facials, body wraps and exfoliation treatments. Fitness center, Jacuzzi and sauna.

BUSINESS SERVICES: Business and concierge services. Complimentary Internet access in guest rooms.

DINING: Home to "The Herbfarm," renowned as one of America's finest dining establishments. The "Barking Frog" features the freshest local ingredients. Seasonal alfresco-style dining in the courtyard.

MEETINGS: Total Meeting Rooms: 5 Total Sq. Ft.: 4,000 / Sq. M.: 372

RATES: USD 260.00 to 750.00; Corporate, Group, Package rates.

Mr. James Simkins,
General Manager

14580 Northeast 145th Street
Woodinville, Washington 98072, U.S.A.
Tel: +1.425.424.3900
Fax: +1.425.424.2585
Email: mail@willowslodge.com
www.willowslodge.com

Worldwide Reservations
www.preferredhotels.com
800.323.7500 U.S.A./Canada
00.800.3237.5001 Europe (UIFN)
Other areas: See page 192

THE DAVENPORT HOTEL

Built in 1912 and meticulously restored to its original grandeur, the hotel reopened in July of 2002. A respect for the past and an eye to the future was applied in the restoration, providing guests with a sense of timelessness as they stroll through the common areas while still offering guests state of the art technology. The hotel is within an easy drive of 76 lakes, five major ski areas and 49 golf courses. Spokane International Airport: 6 miles/9.7 km, 10 minutes.

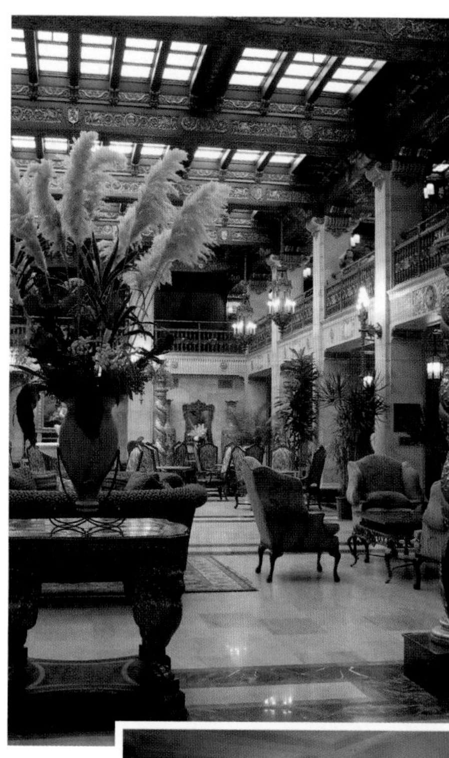

ACCOMMODATIONS: 284 total guestrooms, including 24 suites. All rooms feature hand-carved mahogany furniture, imported Irish linens and Travertine marble baths. Other amenities include 27" flat screen televisions, data port, voice mail and private direct line capability.

FACILITIES/SERVICES: Health and beauty spa, fitness center, indoor pool, concierge, dry cleaning, gift shop, flower shop, candy shop and art gallery.

BUSINESS SERVICES: On-site 24 hour Business Center, wireless Ethernet and high-speed Internet access.

DINING: "The Palm Court," The Davenport's signature restaurant, offers classic Euro-Asian cuisine. The exotic "Peacock Room" is the hotel lounge with adjacent Cigar Room.

MEETINGS: Total Meeting Rooms: 8 Total Sq. Ft.: 25,000 Square Meters: 2,327

RATES: USD 169.00 to 1,950.00; Corporate, Group, Package rates.

Walt & Karen Worthy, Owners/Managers

Lynnelle Caudill, Director of Operations

---

10 South Post Street
Spokane, Washington 99201, U.S.A.
Tel: +1.509.455.8888
Fax: +1.509.624.4455
Email: info@thedavenporthotel.com
www.thedavenporthotel.com

Worldwide Reservations

www.preferredhotels.com
800.323.7500 U.S.A./Canada
00.800.3237.5001 Europe (UIFN)
Other areas: See page 192

THE GREENBRIER®

ACCOMMODATIONS: 739 total guestrooms, including 33 suites, each with two multi-line phones, voice mail, data port, wireless high-speed Internet access in the main hotel, CD player, safe, robes and mini-bar. VCR and fax machines on request.

FACILITIES/SERVICES: Championship golf courses, golf academy, indoor and outdoor tennis, fitness center, spa, falconry, Land Rover Driving School, horseback riding, carriage rides; trap, skeet and sporting clays, whitewater rafting, pools, mountain biking, wingshooting, fishing, kayaking, bowling, croquet; concierge and child care services.

BUSINESS SERVICES: Business Center.

DINING: Four venues offer dining from casual to gourmet.

MEETINGS: Total Meeting Rooms: 35
Total Sq. Ft.: 85,000 / Sq. M.: 7,914

RATES: USD 219.00 to 427.00;
Per person, per day, (double occupancy, breakfast and dinner daily), Corporate, Group and Holiday rates.

Mr. Ted J. Kleisner, President and Managing Director

---

300 West Main Street
White Sulphur Springs, West Virginia
24986, U.S.A.
Tel: +1.304.536.1110
Fax: +1.304.536.7854
Email: the_greenbrier@greenbrier.com
www.greenbrier.com

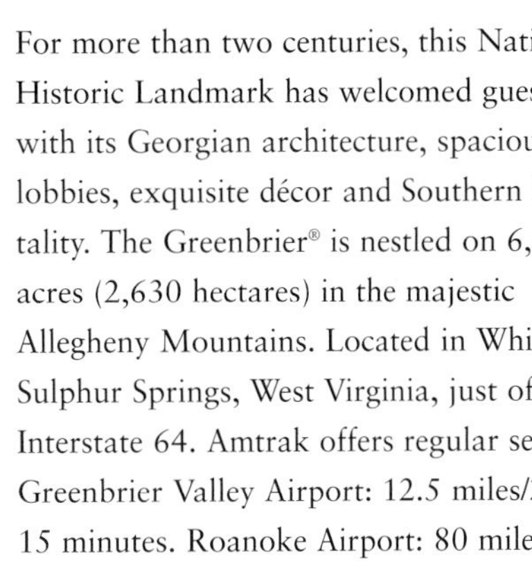

For more than two centuries, this National Historic Landmark has welcomed guests with its Georgian architecture, spacious lobbies, exquisite décor and Southern hospitality. The Greenbrier® is nestled on 6,500 acres (2,630 hectares) in the majestic Allegheny Mountains. Located in White Sulphur Springs, West Virginia, just off Interstate 64. Amtrak offers regular service. Greenbrier Valley Airport: 12.5 miles/20 km, 15 minutes. Roanoke Airport: 80 miles/ 130 km, 1.5 hours.

Worldwide Reservations
www.preferredhotels.com
800.323.7500 U.S.A./Canada
00.800.3237.5001 Europe (UIFN)
Other areas: See page 192

THE PFISTER HOTEL

Built in 1893 as a "palace for the people," The Pfister contains the largest collection of Victorian art of its kind in the world. The Pfister offers luxurious hospitality in the heart of downtown Milwaukee. In the exclusive East Town neighborhood, three blocks from Lake Michigan, close to the Milwaukee Art Museum, convention center, shopping and entertainment. Mitchell Int'l. Airport: 12 miles/19 km, 15 minutes.

ACCOMMODATIONS: 307 total guestrooms, including 82 suites, each with two phones, data port, voice mail, newspaper, safe, in-room coffeemakers and mini-bar. VCR and fax on request.

FACILITIES/SERVICES: 24-hour room service, concierge, dry cleaning, shoe shine, salon, florist, shops, fitness center and indoor pool.

BUSINESS SERVICES: Secretarial services available.

DINING: "Celia" for fine dining, "Café at the Pfister" for contemporary cuisine, "Café Rouge" for champagne brunch and luncheon buffet, the "Lobby Lounge" for afternoon tea, cocktails and entertainment, and "Blu," an upscale, intimate lounge located atop the Pfister tower. 24-hour in-room dining also available.

MEETINGS: Total Meeting Rooms: 18
Total Sq. Ft.: 25,000 / Sq. M.: 2,323

RATES: USD 189.00 to 990.00; Corporate, Group, Package rates.

Mr. John D. Williams,
General Manager

424 East Wisconsin Avenue
Milwaukee, Wisconsin 53202, U.S.A.
Tel: +1.414.273.8222
Fax: +1.414.273.5025
Email: info@thepfisterhotel.com
www.thepfisterhotel.com

Worldwide Reservations

www.preferredhotels.com
800.323.7500 U.S.A./Canada
00.800.3237.5001 Europe (UIFN)
Other areas: See page 192

SNAKE RIVER LODGE & SPA

ACCOMMODATIONS: 88 total guestrooms, including 44 suites, each with two multi-line phones, voice mail, data port, Internet access, complimentary newspaper, safe, robes, hair dryer and refrigerator.

FACILITIES/SERVICES: Spa, concierge services, shoe shine, fitness center, child care services, salon, dry cleaning and shops.

BUSINESS SERVICES: On-site business services available.

DINING: Snake River Lodge & Spa's popular "GameFish Restaurant" features a fusion of Southern and Western cuisine and serves breakfast, lunch and dinner daily.

MEETINGS: Total Meeting Rooms: 4 Total Sq. Ft.: 4,041 / Sq. M.: 376

RATES: USD 150.00 to 1,300.00; Group, Package rates.

Mr. Bruce Grosbety,
General Manager

7710 Granite Look Road, P.O. Box 348
Teton Village, Wyoming 83025, U.S.A.
Tel: +1.307.732.6000
Fax: +1.307.732.6009
Email: info@snakeriverlodge.com
www.snakeriverlodge.com

The closest resort to Grand Teton National Park's south entrance, Snake River Lodge & Spa combines the rustic authenticity of a great lodge with the elegance of a luxury hotel. Faithful to Laurance Rockefeller's vision, guests step outside to enjoy a great ski and snowboard resort, rugged natural beauty, awesome national parks or the western town of Jackson. Guests can enjoy a spa and gourmet dining. Located at the base of Jackson Hole Ski Resort in Teton Village, the Lodge is just 20 minutes from Jackson's Town Square. Jackson Hole Airport: 20 miles/32 km, 25 minutes.

Worldwide Reservations
www.preferredhotels.com
800.323.7500 U.S.A./Canada
00.800.3237.5001 Europe (UIFN)
Other areas: See page 192

CARIBBEAN

SANDY LANE

The resort, which recently underwent major reconstruction and expansion, is set in an ancient mahogany grove overlooking a gorgeous crescent of beach on Barbados' western coast. The architecture is classical Palladian style, like the original building, and the hotel features a luxurious white coral stone rotunda, Italian marble floors, plantation-style furniture and sumptuous décor. Located along the west coast of Barbados, this luxury resort is 8 miles/ 13 km. from Bridgetown. Grantley Adams Int'l. Airport: 8 miles/13 km, 30 minutes.

ACCOMMODATIONS: 112 total guestrooms, including 18 suites, each with two phones, data port, voice mail, fax machine, complimentary newspaper, CD player, safe, mini-bar, robes and hair dryer.

FACILITIES/SERVICES: Spa, concierge services, shoe shine, fitness center, child care services, salon, tennis, dry cleaning, florist, shops, children's center, golf and watersports.

BUSINESS SERVICES: On-site Business Center.

DINING: "Bajan Blue Restaurant" offers all-day dining featuring Mediterranean and Caribbean cuisine. "Passions Restaurant" features an eclectic mix of Carib-Asian and French influence cuisine.

MEETINGS: Total Meeting Rooms: 6 Total Sq. Ft.: 8,000 / Sq. M.: 745

RATES: USD 600.00 to 6,500.00; Group rates.

Mr. Colm Hannon, General Manager

St. James, Barbados
Tel: +1.246.444.2000
Fax: +1.246.444.2222
Email: mail@sandylane.com
www.sandylane.com

Worldwide Reservations

www.preferredhotels.com
800.323.7500 U.S.A./Canada
00.800.3237.5001 Europe (UIFN)
Other areas: *See page 192*

PETER ISLAND RESORT

ACCOMMODATIONS: 54 total guestrooms, including 2 villas, each with phones, data port, voice mail, CD player, safe, mini-bar, robes.

FACILITIES/SERVICES: All water sports, equipment and instruction are complimentary at Peter Island. Spa services, fitness center, tennis courts, hiking trails, horticulture tours, library and yacht service to and from Tortola.

BUSINESS SERVICES: Multi-room villas and open-air lounges provide ideal accommodations for weddings, executive retreats and corporate gatherings. It is possible to rent the entire island, ensuring personal and undivided attention.

DINING: "Tradewinds" prepares sophisticated versions of West Indian dishes and continental classics. Peter Island also offers a stellar Wine Room, "Deadman's Beach Bar & Grill," "Drakes Channel Lounge" and "White Bay Picnic Lunch."

MEETINGS: Total Meeting Rooms: 2
Total Sq. Ft.: 900 / Sq. M.: 84

RATES: USD 530.00 to 7,250.00; Group, Package rates.

Mr. Jeffry Humes, General Manager

P.O. Box 211
Road Town, Tortola, British Virgin Islands
Tel: +1.770.476.9988
Fax: +1.770.476.4979
Email: reservations@peterisland.com
www.peterisland.com

Nestled in a sanctuary of natural beauty, Peter Island offers an island of sheer paradise. Guests enjoy the tropical solitude of 1,200 acres of lush island and stunning beaches, along with exquisite food, spa facilities, private yacht, tennis courts, hiking trails, scuba diving, snorkeling and deep-sea fishing. The largest private island in the BVI, Peter Island is just four miles (6km) south of Tortola and a 25-minute cruise on the resort's private yacht from Beef Island Airport.

Worldwide Reservations
www.preferredhotels.com
800.323.7500 U.S.A./Canada
00.800.3237.5001 Europe (UIFN)
Other areas: See page 192

EUROPE

ANASSA

ACCOMMODATIONS: 177 total guestrooms, including 29 suites, some with outdoor pool or whirlpool, direct dial phone, mini-bar, safe, robes, hair dryer and satellite TV. CD player and VCR in all suites. Fax machine upon request.

FACILITIES/SERVICES: Tennis, squash, water sports, outdoor and indoor pools, thalassotherapy, spa, concierge, child care services and children's club, dry cleaning, shoe shine, salon, wine tasting, jeep safaris, boat trips.

BUSINESS SERVICES: Translating and secretarial services available.

DINING: Each of Anassa's four restaurants, as well as the all-day dining facilities by the pools, offer a scrumptious choice of local and international dishes, using fresh produce from the hotel's own farm.

MEETINGS: Total Meeting Rooms: 3
Total Sq. Ft.: 10,680 / Sq. M.: 994

RATES: CYP 130.00 to 1,815.00; Corporate, Group, Package rates.

Mr. York Brandes, General Manager

P.O. Box 66006
Latchi CY8830, Cyprus
Tel: +357.2.688.8000
Fax: +357.2.632.2900
Email: anassa@thanoshotels.com
www.thanoshotels.com

Anassa's architecture reflects the many aspects of Cyprus' history, with Greek and Roman mosaics and Venetian frescoes. Breathtaking views of the Mediterranean, stunning beaches and cool courtyards make this inviting resort a relaxing hideaway. West of the village of Neo Chorion, overlooking the wild beauty of the Akamas Peninsula, Anassa lies in the unspoiled and largely undiscovered region of Polis. Pafos Int'l. Airport: 31 miles/50 km, 35 minutes.

Worldwide Reservations
www.preferredhotels.com
800.323.7500 U.S.A./Canada
00.800.3237.5001 Europe (UIFN)
Other areas: See page 192

THE ANNABELLE

ACCOMMODATIONS: 218 total guestrooms, including 38 suites, and 11 garden studio suites, each with mini-bar, direct dial phone, radio, safe, robes and satellite TV. Some feature Jacuzzi, CD player and VCR. Fax machines upon request.

FACILITIES/SERVICES: Pools, health & beauty center, tennis court, squash, water sports, children's club, dry cleaning, salon and wine tastings. Golf courses nearby.

BUSINESS SERVICES: Translating and secretarial services available.

DINING: "The Deck" for gourmet cuisine, "Fontana Amorosa" for contemporary cuisine, "The Mediterraneo" for Cypriot and Mediterranean cuisine. "Pergola" hosts theme evenings. The "Lobby Bar" features classical music, "Byzantine" offers cocktails and music.

MEETINGS: Total Meeting Rooms: 5
Total Sq. Ft.: 7,158 / Sq. M.: 666

RATES: CYP 72.00 to 960.00; Corporate, Group, Package rates.

Mr. Richard Lander, General Manager

Poseidonos Avenue
Pafos 8042, Cyprus
Tel: +357.26.938.333
Fax: +357.26.945.502
Email: the-annabelle@thanoshotels.com
www.thanoshotels.com

From the elegant wood and marble of the lobby to the classical decorations and Greek statues of the ballroom, The Annabelle's interiors are utterly peaceful. Set on six acres (two hectares) of lush tropical gardens overlooking the bay and notable archeological sites, The Annabelle treats guests to the genuine friendliness of a family-run hotel. On the southwest coast of Cyprus in Pafos, the birthplace of Aphrodite. Pafos Int'l. Airport: 10 miles/16 km, 15 minutes.

Worldwide Reservations
www.preferredhotels.com
800.323.7500 U.S.A./Canada
00.800.3237.5001 Europe (UIFN)
Other areas: See page 192

HOTEL PALACE PRAHA

Built in 1909 in Art Nouveau style, the hotel features an elegant facade and enchanting interior decoration. The Hotel Palace Praha prides itself on fostering a family atmosphere, offering impeccable personal service and the warmest of welcomes to every guest. Hotel Palace Praha is centrally located on the corner of Panská and Jindrisská streets, adjacent to the famous Wenceslav's Square and the Mustek subway station. Prague Ruzyne Airport: 15 miles/11 km, 20 minutes.

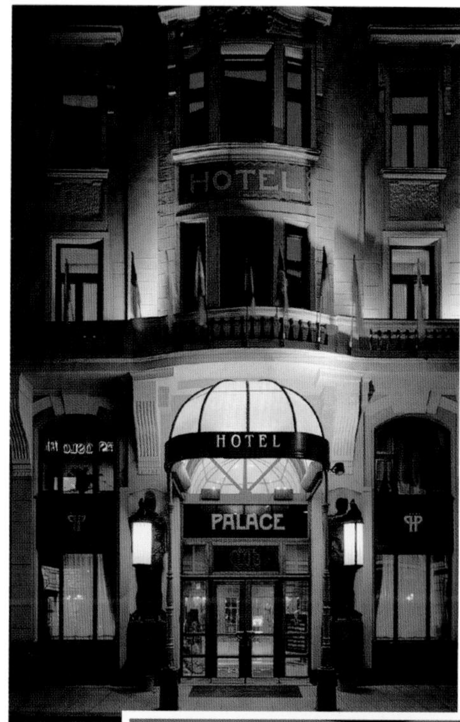

ACCOMMODATIONS: 124 total guestrooms, including 10 suites, each with audio/video equipment, two phones, voice mail, data port, in-room Internet access, trouser press, safe and mini-bar.

FACILITIES/SERVICES: In-house laundry and dry cleaning, exchange office, concierge, child care services, massage, salon, sauna, international newspapers and magazines.

BUSINESS SERVICES: On-site business center, secretarial services, conference center with state-of-the-art technical equipment.

DINING: "Restaurant L'Epoque" features breakfast. The "Gourmet Club Lounge" offers breakfast, lunch, dinner and cocktails. The "Gourmet Club Restaurant" offers a selection of local and international cuisine as well as a unique selection of wines from around the world.

MEETINGS: Total Meeting Rooms: 3
Total Sq. Ft.: 3,950 / Sq. M.: 368

RATES: EUR 295.00 to 850.00; Corporate, Group, Package rates.

Mr. Christopher von Prack,
General Manager

Panská 12
Prague CZ-111 21, Czech Republic
Tel: +420.224.093.111
Fax: +420.224.221.240
Email: palhoprg@palacehotel.cz
www.palacehotel.cz

Worldwide Reservations
www.preferredhotels.com
800.323.7500 U.S.A./Canada
00.800.3237.5001 Europe (UIFN)
Other areas: See page 192

LA TRÉMOILLE

ACCOMMODATIONS: 93 total guestrooms, including 5 suites, each with multi-line phones, voice mail, data port, high-speed Internet access, CD and DVD player, trouser press, safe and mini-bar.

FACILITIES/SERVICES: Concierge, shoe shine, dry cleaning, health club and fitness center. 24-hour room service available.

BUSINESS SERVICES: Secretarial services available through concierge. Fax machines available in rooms upon request.

DINING: Our new restaurant and bar "Senso," designed and managed by Sir Terence Conran, offers an inventive international cuisine in an exciting décor.

MEETINGS: Total Meeting Rooms: 2 Total Sq. Ft.: 646 / Sq. M.: 60

RATES: EUR 398.00 to 948.00; Corporate, Group, Package rates.

Mr. Augustin Benetti,
General Manager

14, rue de la Trémoille
Paris 75 008, France
Tel: +33.1.56.52.14.00
Fax: +33.1.40.70.01.08
Email: reservation@hotel-tremoille.com
www.hotel-tremoille.com

La Trémoille has been fully renovated in 2002. Located on Paris' Right Bank in the Haute Couture district, La Trémoille is set in a traditional Haussmann building just off the River Seine. Built in the 19th century, the hotel retains much of its original elegance and charm with a subtle blend of traditional and contemporary styles. Ideally situated on a quiet street in the "Triangle d'Or," in the heart of the 8th Arrondissement, within walking distance of the Champs-Élysées, Arc de Triomphe, Eiffel Tower and the famous shops of the Avenue Montaigne. Paris Roissy-CDG Airport: 15 miles/25 km, 45 minutes.

Worldwide Reservations
www.preferredhotels.com
800.323.7500 U.S.A./Canada
00.800.3237.5001 Europe (UIFN)
Other areas: See page 192

MONTALEMBERT

Montalembert recently unveiled a new look while maintaining the spirit of the original. The interior décor has been enriched by new materials and colors: white leather armchairs, grey velvet sofas, tobacco cream fabrics, and taupe and lilac accents. Situated on a quiet side street, near the crossroad of Rue Du Bac and Boulevard Saint-Germain, Montalembert provides easy access to some of the finest galleries, boutiques, cafés and antique shops of the Left Bank. The Louvre and the Musee d' Orsay are a short walk away. Paris Orly Airport: 11 miles/18 km, 30 minutes.

Worldwide Reservations

www.preferredhotels.com

800.323.7500 U.S.A./Canada

00.800.3237.5001 Europe (UIFN)

Other areas: See page 192

ACCOMMODATIONS: 56 total guestrooms, including 8 suites, each featuring audio/video equipment (TV, VCR, CD player), fully equipped marble bathroom, fax and computer connections, safe and mini-bar.

FACILITIES/SERVICES: Same-day laundry and dry cleaning service, 24-hour room service, video library, concierge, high-speed Internet access via wireless card, and underground parking.

BUSINESS SERVICES: Business center available on request.

DINING: Watch Parisian life roll past from the outdoor dining terrace of the newly refurbished "Le Restaurant," open all day long around a new food and service concept. Or sit back and enjoy the latest cocktails by the open wood-burning fire of the "Library Bar."

MEETINGS: Total Meeting Rooms: 1 Total Sq. Ft.: 398 / Sq. M.: 37

RATES: EUR 320.00 to 1,150.00; Package rates.

Mr. Thierry Dechaux,
General Manager

---

3 Rue de Montalembert
Paris 75007, France
Tel: +33.14.549.6868
Fax: +33.14.549.6949
Email: welcome@montalembert.com
www.montalembert.com

HOTEL BAYERISCHER HOF

With more than 160 years of tradition, this historic hotel offers a variety of unique guestrooms and banqueting facilities. Located in the heart of Munich, it is among the grand hotels of the world. Across from the Frauenkirche Cathedral and an easy walk to business, shopping and cultural sites. Munich Int'l. Airport: 22 miles/35 km, 45 minutes.

ACCOMMODATIONS: 395 total guestrooms, including 49 suites, each with two phones, data port, voice mail, Internet access, mini-bar, safe, robes and multimedia TV with Sony PlayStation. VCR on request.

FACILITIES/SERVICES: Indoor/outdoor pool, sauna, solarium, steam bath, massage, cardio fitness center, child care services, dry cleaning, salon, theater and shops.

BUSINESS SERVICES: On-site Business Center, secretarial and translating services available.

DINING: Enjoy Polynesian food and drinks at "Trader Vic's," international and regional cuisine at the "Garden-Restaurant," or Bavarian specialties in the "Palais Keller."

MEETINGS: Total Meeting Rooms: 35 Total Sq. Ft.: 48,935 / Sq. M.: 4,556

RATES: EUR 208.00 to 1,430.00; Corporate, Group, Package rates.

Ms. Innegrit Volkhardt,
Managing Owner

2-6 Promenadeplatz
Munich 80333, Germany
Tel: +49.89.21200
Fax: +49.89.2120906
Email: info@bayerischerhof.de
www.bayerischerhof.de

Worldwide Reservations
www.preferredhotels.com
800.323.7500 U.S.A./Canada
00.800.3237.5001 Europe (UIFN)
Other areas: *See page 192*

DROMOLAND CASTLE HOTEL

This historic 16th-century castle was originally the stronghold of the High King of Ireland, Brian Boru. Nestled on 370 acres (150 hectares) of forest and parkland, and forted by its own private lake, this majestic hotel is also warm and intimate, with log fires glowing throughout the public areas. Six miles (10 km) from the town of Ennis, 18 miles (29 km) from the city of Limerick. Ennis Train Station: 6 miles/10 km, Limerick Station: 18 miles/29 km. Shannon Int'l. Airport: 8 miles/13 km, 15 minutes.

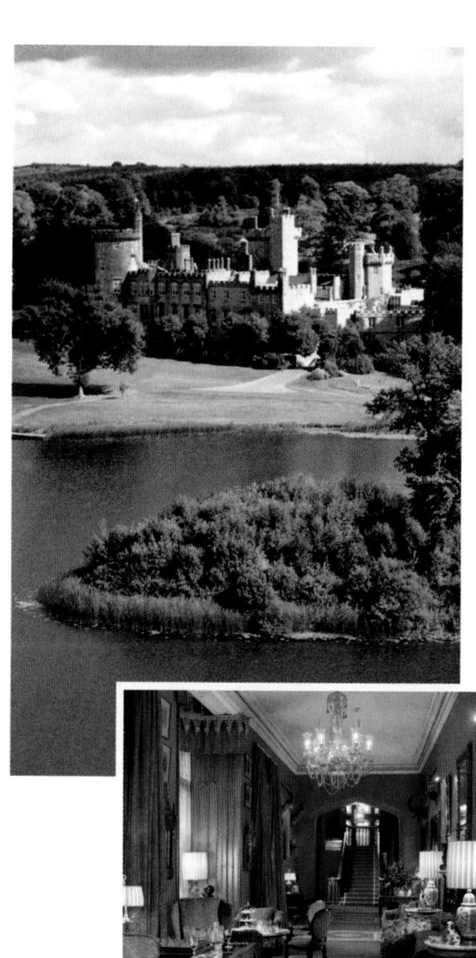

ACCOMMODATIONS: 100 total guestrooms, including 6 suites, each with phones, data port, voice mail, bathrobes, slippers, complimentary Celtic Crossing liqueur, trouser press, iron & board, television, stereo & selection of CDs, VCR (videos available from reception), safe, hair dryer and complimentary postcards.

FACILITIES/SERVICES: Pool, spa, fitness center, tennis, concierge, child care services, dry cleaning, shoe shine, salon, golf course and jogging trails.

BUSINESS SERVICES: Business Center, secretarial and translating services and complimentary Internet access.

DINING: Choose from "Earl of Thomond Restaurant" for gourmet dining or the brasserie-style "Fig Tree Restaurant."

MEETINGS: Total Meeting Rooms: 5 Total Sq. Ft.: 5,088 / Sq. M.: 474

RATES: EUR 204.00 to 1,186.00; Corporate, Group, Package rates.

Mr. Mark Nolan, General Manager

Newmarket-on-Fergus
County Clare, Ireland
Tel: +353.6.136.8144
Fax: +353.6.136.3355
Email: sales@dromoland.ie
www.dromoland.ie

Worldwide Reservations
www.preferredhotels.com
800.323.7500 U.S.A./Canada
00.800.3237.5001 Europe (UIFN)
Other areas: See page 192

THE K CLUB

ACCOMMODATIONS: 79 total guestrooms, including 24 suites, each with two phones, voice mail, satellite TV, newspaper, robes, safe, fresh fruit, handmade chocolates, mineral water and VCR.

FACILITIES/SERVICES: 18-hole championship golf course, spa, fitness center, river and course fishing, horseback riding, clay-target shooting, concierge, child care services, dry cleaning, salon, florist, shoe shine and shops. Golf and fishing classes available.

BUSINESS SERVICES: Secretarial service available.

DINING: "The Byerley Turk" offers fine dining blending French and Irish cuisine. The "Legends Restaurant" in the golf club offers à la carte choices in a relaxed atmosphere. 24-hour in-room and private dining available.

MEETINGS: Total Meeting Rooms: 4
Total Sq. Ft.: 4,844 / Sq. M.: 451

RATES: EUR 270.00 to 410.00; Corporate, Group, Package rates.

Mr. Ray Carroll, Chief Executive

At Straffan
County Kildare, Ireland
Tel: +353.1601.7200
Fax: +353.1601.7299
Email: resortsales@kclub.ie
www.kclub.ie

Combining the elegance and unique charm of an Irish country house, The K Club is an elegantly restored 19th-century mansion estate nestled among 700 acres (283 hectares) of lush countryside. Guests will enjoy the luxurious surroundings of this warm, charming and intimate setting. On the River Liffey, 17 miles (27 km) southwest of Dublin. Venue for the Smurfit European Open and the Ryder Cup in 2006. Dublin Int'l. Airport: 15 miles/24 km, 30 minutes.

Worldwide Reservations
www.preferredhotels.com
800.323.7500 U.S.A./Canada
00.800.3237.5001 Europe (UIFN)
Other areas: See page 192

AGHADOE HEIGHTS HOTEL

Aghadoe Heights Hotel is a haven of gracious elegance, a treasure chest of antiques and an example of contemporary design, all combined with Irish charm. The hotel prides itself on its personal service and its ability to combine the luxuries of an international hotel with the touches of a country home. In beautiful County Kerry, perched on the hill of Aghadoe overlooking the Lakes of Killarney. Kerry Airport: 9 miles/14 km, 15 minutes. Shannon Int'l. Airport: 78 miles/125 km, 2 hours.

ACCOMMODATIONS: 63 total guestrooms, including 9 suites, each with three phones, newspaper, mini-bar, bathrobe, slippers, fresh fruit, handmade chocolates, flowers, mineral water, trouser press and satellite TV. Fax machine on request.

FACILITIES/SERVICES: Leisure center, swimming pool, sauna, plunge pool, solarium, Jacuzzi, fitness room, tennis, massage/treatment rooms, child care services, dry cleaning, concierge, limousine, jogging and walking trails, salon and valet parking.

BUSINESS SERVICES: On-site Business Center, complimentary Internet access, secretarial services and car rental services.

DINING: "Fredricks at the Heights" is renowned for its exquisite cuisine, including a full Irish breakfast and an extensive dinner menu. The "Heights" lounge offers a snack menu daily.

MEETINGS: Total Meeting Rooms: 3 Total Sq. Ft.: 2,861 / Sq. M.: 266

RATES: EUR 250.00 to 786.00; Corporate, Group, Package rates.

Pat and Marie Chawke,
General Managers

Lakes of Killarney
Killarney, County Kerry, Ireland
Tel: +353.643.1766
Fax: +353.643.1345
Email: info@aghadoeheights.com
www.aghadoeheights.com

Worldwide Reservations
www.preferredhotels.com
800.323.7500 U.S.A./Canada
00.800.3237.5001 Europe (UIFN)
Other areas: See page 192

PALAZZO ARZAGA HOTEL, SPA & GOLF RESORT

ACCOMMODATIONS: 84 total guestrooms, including 3 suites, one junior suite, two fresco rooms, 14 executive rooms, 24 deluxe rooms, 40 classic rooms. Some suites feature hand-painted ceilings, and all rooms feature mini-bar, safe, robes, data port, voice mail, hair dryer and satellite TV.

FACILITIES/SERVICES: Spa, thermal pool, treatment rooms, outdoor pool, tennis courts, golf with Jack Nicklaus II course and Gary Player course and pro shop. Home of Arzaga Golf Academy, a teaching and learning center of the PGA of Europe. Child care center is available.

BUSINESS SERVICES: Business facilities, airline ticketing and car rental.

DINING: Fine dining at "Il Moretto," featuring authentic atmosphere dishes. The "Clubhouse" offers buffet menus in a relaxed ambiance.

MEETINGS: Total Meeting Rooms: 5
Total Sq. Ft.: 3,918 / Sq. M.: 365

RATES: EUR 278.00 to 900.00; Corporate, Group, Package rates.

Mr. Giampaolo Burattin,
Hotel Manager

25080 Carzago di Calvagese della Riviera
Brescia, Italy
Tel: +39.030.680600
Fax: +39.030.6806270
Email: arzaga@arzaga.it
www.palazzoarzaga.com

A 15th-century historic palazzo with internal courtyard and chapel nestled in the beautiful hills of Lake Garda. Many rooms retain the original frescoes, hand-painted ceilings and marble fireplaces. Guests will relax in the tranquility of history and style. Situated in the province of Brescia. Only 20 minutes from Brescia-Montichiari Airport: 8 miles/ 20 km. 30 minutes from Verona-Catullo Airport: 27 miles/44 km. 90 minutes from Milan and 120 minutes from Venice.

Worldwide Reservations
www.preferredhotels.com
800.323.7500 U.S.A./Canada
00.800.3237.5001 Europe (UIFN)
Other areas: See page 192

EXCELSIOR PALACE HOTEL

Recently restored, this luxury hotel dates back to 1901 and perfectly combines its turn-of-the-century style with the comforts of a contemporary property. Uniquely located, overlooking the stunning Portofino Coast and the pretty bay of Rapallo, the hotel enjoys a breathtaking panoramic position. Experience the intimate beauty of this relaxing hideway and its timeless elegance. Close to the well-known fishing village of Portofino and not far from the Cinque Terre area, part of UNESCO heritage. Genoa Airport: 20 miles/32 km, 45 minutes

Worldwide Reservations
www.preferredhotels.com
800.323.7500 U.S.A./Canada
00.800.3237.5001 Europe (UIFN)
Other areas: *See page 192*

ACCOMMODATIONS: 131 total guestrooms, including 17 suites, each with two phones, high-speed Internet access, VCR on request, newspaper, safe, mini-bar, robes, hair dryer, slippers and satellite TV. CD player and fax machine available on request.

FACILITIES/SERVICES: Spa, concierge, shoe shine, fitness center, child care services, salon and dry cleaning.

BUSINESS SERVICES: Business Center and secretarial services.

DINING: "Lord Byron Restaurant" for the finest Italian food, "Eden Roc" in summer for local dishes with fresh fish. "Yachting Bar" for cocktails and "Sporting Bar" by the pool for low-calorie snacks and salads.

MEETINGS: Total Meeting Rooms: 9 Total Sq. Ft.: 6,997 / Sq. M.: 650

RATES: EUR 162.00 to 1,400.00; Corporate, Group, Package rates.

Mr. Aldo Werdin, General Manager

Via San Michele di Pagana, 8
16035 Rapallo, Portofino Coast, Italy
Tel: +39.0185.230666
Fax: +39.0185.230214
Email: excelsior@thi.it
www.excelsiorpalace.thi.it

PALAZZO SASSO

ACCOMMODATIONS: 44 total guestrooms, including 6 suites, most with Jacuzzi bath, two phones, Internet connection, safe, hair dryer, mini-bar and robes. VCR on request.

FACILITIES/SERVICES: Rooftop sun terrace, swimming pool, tennis, hydromassage plunge pools, Internet station, concierge, garage, child care services, dry cleaning, shoe shine and massage. Planned private tours upon request.

BUSINESS SERVICES: Internet access available in the library. Secretarial and translating services available.

DINING: "Rossellinis" for Italian haute cuisine and "Caffé dell' Arte" for an array of local specialties.

MEETINGS: Total Meeting Rooms: 1 Total Sq. Ft.: 1,033 / Sq. M.: 96

RATES: EUR 200.00 to 1,350.00

Mr. Attilio Marro, General Manager

Via San Giovanni del Toro, 28
Ravello 84010, Italy
Tel: +39.08.981.8181
Fax: +39.08.985.8900
Email: info@palazzosasso.com
www.palazzosasso.com

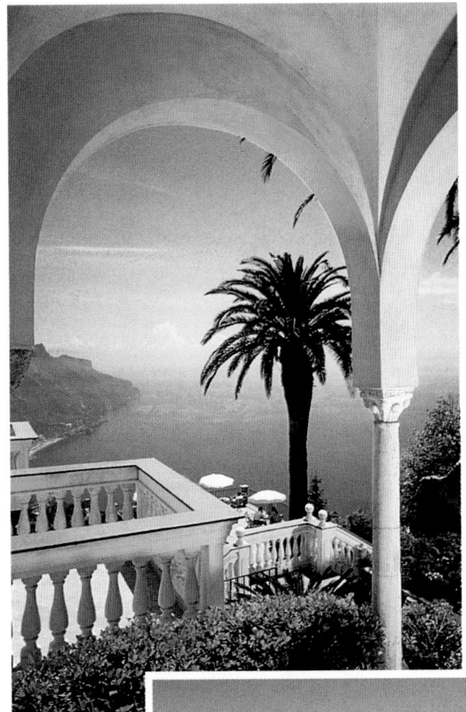

An elegant 12th-century villa situated on a clifftop 1,000 feet (305 meters) above the sparkling Mediterranean on the breathtaking Amalfi Coast. The historic hotel possesses a sense of timeless elegance — a civilized ambiance with a modern edge. On the Amalfi Coast close to the fishing village of Positano. Naples Airport: 37 miles/60 km, 90 minutes.

Worldwide Reservations

www.preferredhotels.com

800.323.7500 U.S.A./Canada

00.800.3237.5001 Europe (UIFN)

Other areas: See page 192

HOTEL DE RUSSIE

Located on the fashionable Via del Babuino facing the Piazza del Popolo, the Hotel de Russie is walking distance from the Spanish Steps. The simple, elegant décor, romantic terraced gardens and spectacular spa facilities provide a peaceful retreat from the hustle and bustle of the Eternal City. Beautiful accommodations, fine cuisine and personalized service are signatures of this historic hotel. The hotel abuts the Villa Borghese, with terraced gardens, and is within walking distance of key sights, fashion houses and the Via Condotti. Rome Fiumicino Airport: 16 miles/25 km, 45 minutes.

Worldwide Reservations

www.preferredhotels.com

800.323.7500 U.S.A./Canada

00.800.3237.5001 Europe (UIFN)

Other areas: See page 192

ACCOMMODATIONS: 125 total guestrooms, including 31 suites, each with state-of-the-art phone system, data port, voice mail, interactive TV and DVD in all suites, fax connection, safe and mini-bar.

FACILITIES/SERVICES: De Russie Spa, gym, same-day laundry, valet parking, concierge and airport transfer available.

BUSINESS SERVICES: On-site Business Center with secretarial services.

DINING: "Le Jardin du Russie Restaurant" and the "Stravinskij Bar" open to the gardens for alfresco dining and offers traditional Italian cuisine.

MEETINGS: Total Meeting Rooms: 5
Total Sq. Ft.: 2,225 / Sq. M.: 207

RATES: EUR 380.00 to 2,300.00; Corporate, Package rates.

Mr. Matthew Dixon,
General Manager

Via del Babuino, 9
Rome 00187, Italy
Tel: +39.06.328881
Fax: +39.06.3288.8888
Email: reservations@hotelderussie.it
www.roccofortehotels.com

Opening Spring 2003

SAN CLEMENTE PALACE

ACCOMMODATIONS: 205 total guestrooms, including 89 suites, each with two phones, data port, high-speed Internet access, VCR available on request, newspaper, safe, mini-bar, robes and hair dryer. Fax machine available in suites.

FACILITIES/SERVICES: Beauty & Wellness Club, tennis courts, a scenic outdoor pool, and a three-hole executive golf course to offer the hotel's exclusive clientele a chance to unwind in contact with nature.

BUSINESS SERVICES: On-site Business Center, secretarial services and translating services available.

DINING: Four restaurants located on the most attractive points of the island offer tempting fare of the Mediterranean culinary tradition.

MEETINGS: Total Meeting Rooms: 6 Total Sq. Ft.: 5,791 / Sq. M.: 538

RATES: EUR 310.00 to 930.00; Corporate, Group, Package rates.

Mr. Maurizio D'Este,
General Manager

Isola di San Clemente
San Marco 30124
Venice, Italy
Tel: +39.041.2413484
Fax: +39.041.2960083
Email: sanclemente@thi.it
www.sanclemente.thi.it

The restoration has made it possible to preserve the historical flavor of the Renaissance and to achieve a luxurious hotel for guests who expect the best. Venice's new luxury hotel, exclusively located on the island of San Clemente, is an oasis of peace, with an enchanting view of the lagoon. Centrally located only a few minutes away from St. Mark's Square by the 24-hour complimentary shuttle boat, 15 minutes away from both the car park and railway station. Marco Polo Int'l. Airport: 10 miles/16 km, 30 minutes.

Worldwide Reservations
www.preferredhotels.com
800.323.7500 U.S.A./Canada
00.800.3237.5001 Europe (UIFN)
Other areas: See page 192

GRAND HOTEL HUIS TER DUIN

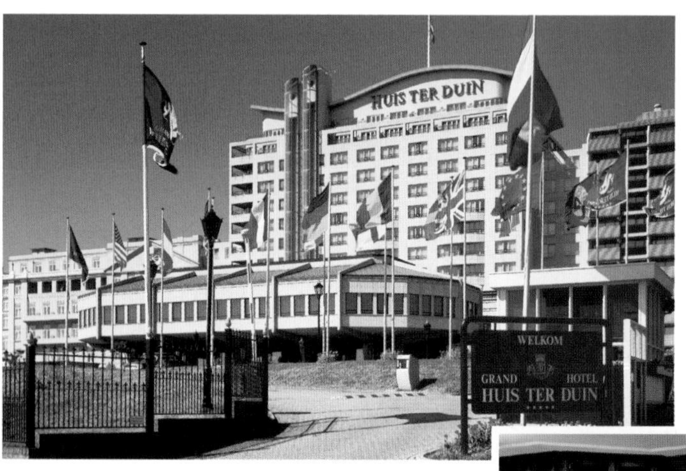

The fashionable Grand Hotel Huis ter Duin has a long-established international reputation. Superbly situated in the dunes directly on the beach, this majestic hotel offers a marvelous view of the North Sea. The shine of polished marble and natural stone reflects the grandeur of the entrance, lobby and public rooms. Centrally located between Amsterdam and The Hague, on the highest top of the dunes of Noordwijk adjacent to the beach and overlooking the North Sea. Schipol Airport: 20 miles/32 km, 30 minutes.

Worldwide Reservations

www.preferredhotels.com

800.323.7500 U.S.A./Canada

00.800.3237.5001 Europe (UIFN)

Other areas: *See page 192*

ACCOMMODATIONS: 254 total guestrooms, including 22 suites, and 4 penthouses, each offering modern conveniences, with views of the North Sea or the charming surroundings of Noordwijk.

FACILITIES/SERVICES: Laundry service, indoor pool, sauna, Turkish health bath, fitness center, massage, solarium, spa, salon, billiard room, mini-golf, tennis, beach pavilion, concierge, shuttle service and heliport.

BUSINESS SERVICES: Business Center.

DINING: The prestigious "Restaurant Latour" serves French cuisine; "La Terrasse" serves casual lunches or dinners; "Van Diepeningen Lounge," "Bar Maritime" and "Club the Conversation" serve cocktails.

MEETINGS: Total Meeting Rooms: 19 Total Sq. Ft.: 41,505 / Sq. M.: 3,864

RATES: EUR 230.00 to 1,300.00; Corporate, Group, Package rates.

Mr. Stephan J. A. B. Stokkermans, Commercial Director

Koningin Astrid Blvd. 5, P.O. Box 85, 2200 AB
Noordwijk aan Zee, The Netherlands
Tel: +31.71.361.9220
Fax: +31.71.361.9401
Email: info@huisterduin.com
www.huisterduin.com

THE SAN ROQUE CLUB

ACCOMMODATIONS: 100 total guestrooms, including 50 suites, all overlooking either the pool or gardens. Each features newspaper, VCR on request, safe, mini-bar, robes and hair dryer.

FACILITIES/SERVICES: Heated lagoon pool, championship golf course and tennis courts. Mediterranean yacht and boat excursions to Morocco; organized excursions to Seville, Jerez, Cordoba and Grand Andalucia Equestrian Centre. Seve Ballesteros Natural Golf School, children's program.

BUSINESS SERVICES: Secretarial services and translating services available.

DINING: "El Bolero" offers the traditional tastes of Andalucia with modern cuisine, both indoor and alfresco. "Kama Kura" features Japanese teppanyaki and sushi. "Buganvilla" outdoor lagoon poolside restaurant.

MEETINGS: Total Meeting Rooms: 1 Total Sq. Ft.: 689 / Sq. M.: 64

RATES: EUR 151.00 to 397.00; Group, Package rates.

Mr. Karl Braun, General Manager

C.N. 340, Km 127
San Roque 11360, Spain
Tel: +34.95.661.3030
Fax: +34.95.661.3012
Email: hotelres@sanroqueclub.com
www.sanroqueclub.com

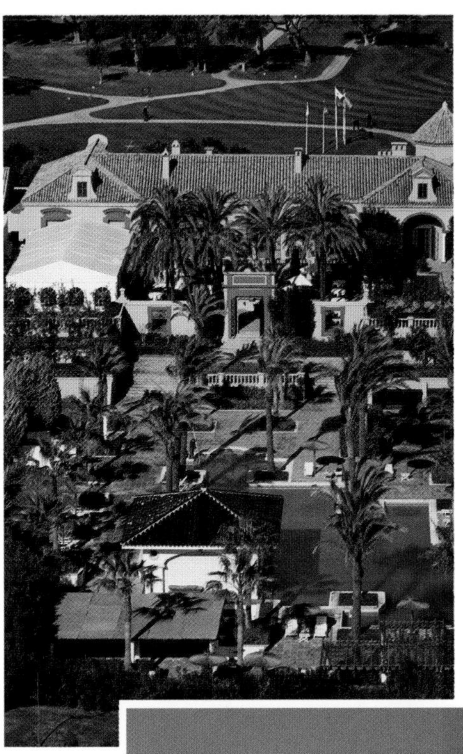

This magnificent mansion, former home of the Domecq sherry dynasty, has been converted into a beautiful hotel, set among the cobbled courtyards and Moorish arcades and pools. Manicured paths lead to the hacienda-style bungalows and to the magnificent lagoon pool. The property is nestled in the heart of one of Spain's finest nature reserves. Between Jerez and Marbella, at the tip of the Iberian peninsula and close to Morocco. Gibraltar Airport: 9 miles/15 km, 15 minutes. Malaga Airport: 62 miles/100 km, 1 hour.

Worldwide Reservations
www.preferredhotels.com
800.323.7500 U.S.A./Canada
00.800.3237.5001 Europe (UIFN)
Other areas: See page 192

BEAU-RIVAGE, GENEVA

Built in 1865, the very private Beau-Rivage still plays host to those who shape our world. Charm and discretion combine with subtlety, efficient service, modern comfort and amenities, making this unique hotel one of the most distinguished addresses in Switzerland. It boasts magnificent views of the lake and the Alps, just a stroll away from the shopping and business district. In the city center, facing the lake and Mont Blanc. Close to the United Nations. International Airport (Geneva Cointrin): 3 miles/5 km, 15 minutes.

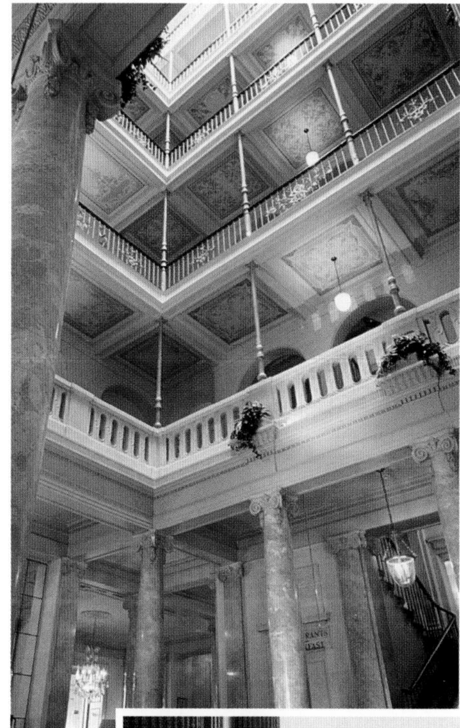

ACCOMMODATIONS: 93 total guestrooms, including 14 suites, each with two multi-line phones, data port, voice mail, fax, newspaper, safe, robes, cable TV and VOD system, Internet connection and video-conference on request; VCR on request.

FACILITIES/SERVICES: Child care services, concierge, dry cleaning, shoe shine, limousine service and multilingual concierge.

BUSINESS SERVICES: Business Center and secretarial services.

DINING: "Le Chat-Botte," a world-renowned French restaurant; "Atrium Bar," open throughout the year; "Patara," fine Thai cuisine restaurant. Each venue offers an exquisite gastronomic experience.

MEETINGS: Total Meeting Rooms: 6 Total Sq. Ft.: 5,522 / Sq. M.: 514

RATES: CHF 395.00 to 3,150.00; Corporate, Group, Package rates.

Mr. Jacques Mayer,
Managing Director

---

13 Quai du Mont-Blanc
Geneva CH-1201, Switzerland
Tel: +41.22.716.6666
Fax: +41.22.716.6060
Email: info@beau-rivage.ch
www.beau-rivage.ch

Worldwide Reservations
www.preferredhotels.com
800.323.7500 U.S.A./Canada
00.800.3237.5001 Europe (UIFN)
Other areas: See page 192

GRAND HOTEL NATIONAL

ACCOMMODATIONS: 60 total guestrooms, including 12 suites, each with multi-line phones, data port, voice mail, Internet access, VCR on request, newspaper, safe, mini-bar, robes and hair dryer. All lakeside rooms feature balcony and marvelous views.

FACILITIES/SERVICES: Indoor pool with sun terrace, sauna, solarium, massage, state-of-the-art fitness center. Concierge, child care services, dry cleaning, shoe shine and limousine service.

BUSINESS SERVICES: Business Corner with Internet access.

DINING: "Le Trianon" for Mediterranean cuisine, "Padrino" for Italian, or the "Thai-Lotus" for Thai specialities. Charming Viennese coffee shop with different specialities and famous piano bar.

MEETINGS: Total Meeting Rooms: 7 Total Sq. Ft.: 6,302 / Sq. M.: 587

RATES: CHF 265.00 to 2,500.00; Corporate, Group, Package rates.

Mr. Josef Müller, General Manager

Haldenstrasse 4
Lucerne CH-6006, Switzerland
Tel: +41.41.419.0909
Fax: +41.41.419.0910
Email: info@national-luzern.ch
www.national-luzern.ch

Established in 1871 and built in the style of a French Renaissance palace, the Grand Hotel National combines the elegance and tradition of a luxury hotel with charming Swiss hospitality. It is still inspired by the examples of Cäsar Ritz and Auguste Escoffier during the years 1881-1888, when they managed the hotel. Beautifully situated on the shore of Lake Lucerne in the heart of the historical city center and next to the shopping district. Zurich Int'l. Airport: 40 miles/ 64 km, 60 minutes.

Worldwide Reservations
www.preferredhotels.com
800.323.7500 U.S.A./Canada
00.800.3237.5001 Europe (UIFN)
Other areas: See page 192

PARK HOTEL VITZNAU

A fairy-tale castle with gabled roofs and romantic balconies built in the Belle Epoque style in 1903. Park Hotel Vitznau lies on the shores of deep-blue Lake Lucerne between Alpine peaks and vast green meadows. Guests will enjoy a relaxed atmosphere at this elegant and spacious hideaway. Located in Vitznau at the foot of Mount Rigi near Lucerne. Half an hour by car or one hour by paddleboat steamer. Zurich Int'l. Airport: 37 miles/60 km, 60 minutes by car.

ACCOMMODATIONS: 104 total guestrooms, including 33 suites, most with mini-bar, safe, robes, hair dryer, data port, voice mail and ISDN connections. Fax and VCR upon request.

FACILITIES/SERVICES: Heated indoor/outdoor pool, sauna, steam bath, massage, energy therapy, fitness center, hiking, biking, concierge services, child care services, dry cleaning, shoe shine and nearby salon. Spa, golf, fishing, scuba diving, snorkeling, windsurfing and horseback riding nearby.

BUSINESS SERVICES: On-site Business Center, secretarial services and translating services available.

DINING: The "Panoramarestaurant," with a breathtaking view of Lake Lucerne, offers international cuisine. The restaurant "Quatre Cantons," on the garden level, offers contemporary cuisine. Both have musical entertainment. The pool terrace offers lunch, snacks and charcoal-grilled dishes.

MEETINGS: Total Meeting Rooms: 11
Total Sq. Ft.: 1,560 / Sq. M.: 145

RATES: CHF 355.00 to 2,000.00; Group rates.

Mr. Peter Bally, Managing Director

Vitznau CH-6354, Switzerland
Tel: +41.41.399.60.60
Fax: +41.41.399.60.70
Email: info@parkhotel-vitznau.ch
www.parkhotel-vitznau.ch

Worldwide Reservations
www.preferredhotels.com
800.323.7500 U.S.A./Canada
00.800.3237.5001 Europe (UIFN)
Other areas: See page 192

THE CARLTON HOTEL

ACCOMMODATIONS: 105 total guestrooms, including 6 suites, each with complimentary newspaper, safe, mini-bar, TV, radio and hairdryer.

FACILITIES/SERVICES: Spa, health club, concierge, child care services, shoe shine, dry cleaning and salon.

BUSINESS SERVICES: Secretarial services available.

DINING: "Restaurant Le Romanoff" is an elegant dining room where the stunning views provide a perfect accompaniment to culinary delights; "Restaurant Tschine," a cozy à la carte restaurant, featuring regional and international cuisine. The hotel also features a bar with fireplace and piano.

MEETINGS: Total Meeting Rooms: 4 Total Sq. Ft.: 4,844 / Sq. M.: 451

RATES: CHF 170.00 to 2,100.00; Group, Package rates.

Mr. Dominic Bachofen,
General Manager

Via J. Badrutt 11
St. Moritz 7500, Switzerland
Tel: +41.81.836.70.00
Fax: +41.81.836.70.01
Email: info@carlton-stmoritz.ch
www.carlton-stmoritz.ch

This elegant building was built in 1913 in a remarkably beautiful setting. The completely renovated hotel blends tradition, personalized service and modern sophistication. Located in the sunniest area of St. Moritz, a few minutes walk from the village center, the rooms offer spectacular views of the St. Moritz lake and mountains. Within five minutes walking distance to the city center, shopping, restaurants, bars, cinema and casino. Zurich Airport: 125 miles/200 km, 3 hours. Samedan Airport: 4 miles/6 km, 10 minutes.

Worldwide Reservations
www.preferredhotels.com
800.323.7500 U.S.A./Canada
00.800.3237.5001 Europe (UIFN)
Other areas: See page 192

GRAND HOTEL ZERMATTERHOF

Set in a private park with a view of the Matterhorn, this historic hotel has recently been renovated to satisfy every guest expectation. Designed to complement its Alpine furnishings, two-thirds of the rooms offer majestic mountain views. In the center of Zermatt, close to skiing, shopping and nightlife. Milano Airport: 137 miles/ 220 km, 180 minutes. Geneva Airport: 155 miles/250 km, 180 minutes.

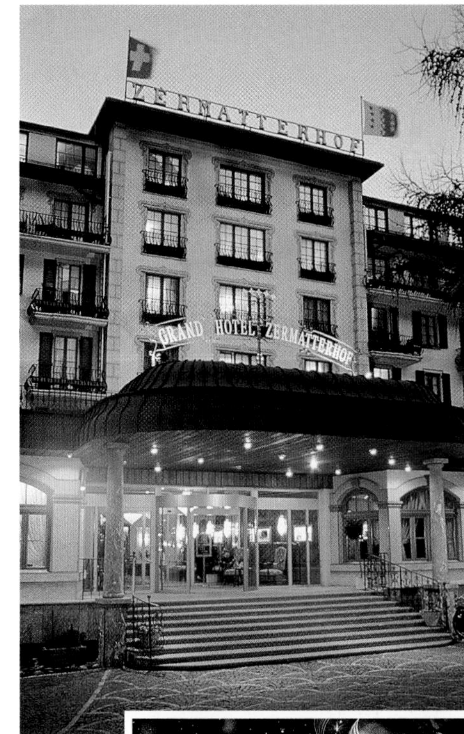

ACCOMMODATIONS: 84 total guestrooms, including 26 suites, each with phones, voice mail, data port, safe, robes and mini-bar. VCR on request.

FACILITIES/SERVICES: Indoor pool, Jacuzzi, sauna, steam room, massage, fitness center, concierge, casino and child care services.

BUSINESS SERVICES: Limited business services available.

DINING: Choose from three restaurants and three bars, including formal dining in "Prato Borni," excellent French cuisine at "La Broche" and alfresco dining in "Le Jardin."

MEETINGS: Total Meeting Rooms: 5
Total Sq. Ft.: 5,400 / Sq. M.: 503

RATES: CHF 290.00 to 1,850.00; Corporate, Group, Package rates.

Mr. Jean-Pierre Lanz,
General Manager

Bahnhofstrasse 55
Postfach 14 CH-3920
Zermatt, Switzerland
Tel: +41.27.966.6600
Fax: +41.27.966.6699
Email: zermatterhof@zermatt.ch
www.zermatt.ch/zermatterhof

Worldwide Reservations

www.preferredhotels.com
800.323.7500 U.S.A./Canada
00.800.3237.5001 Europe (UIFN)
Other areas: *See page 192*

BLAKES HOTEL

Recognized as "the original boutique hotel," Blakes is Anouska Hempel's personal statement about what design can achieve, and reflects individuality, intimacy and stylish creativity. Blakes is now established as the blueprint for the "fashionable small hotel," not only in London, but in cities around the world. Located in South Kensington/Chelsea. Heathrow Int'l Airport: 15 miles/24 km, 40 minutes. 10 minutes from Victoria Station.

ACCOMMODATIONS: 49 total guestrooms, including 9 suites, each individually decorated by Anouska Hempel, the internationally renowned designer. Each is unique; every detail reconstructed to provide the ideal blend of colour, texture and atmosphere, providing an exciting new experience for guests.

FACILITIES/SERVICES: Concierge, valet, child care services, dry cleaning, 24-hour room service, tennis, fitness center and spa nearby.

BUSINESS SERVICES: Private faxes, satellite TV, VCR, hi-fi system, safe, and other high-tech equipment for modern living.

DINING: "Blakes Restaurant" has an unrivalled reputation for its menus' superb originality; the bar is popular, lively and full of character.

MEETINGS: Total Meeting Rooms: 1
Total Sq. Ft.: 344 / Sq. M.: 32

RATES: GBP 255.00 to 895.00; Corporate, Group, Package rates.

Mr. Edward Wauters,
General Manager

---

33 Roland Gardens
London SW7 3PF, United Kingdom
Tel: +44.207.370.6701
Fax: +44.207.373.0442
Email: blakes-sales@easynet.co.uk
www.blakeshotel.com

Worldwide Reservations
www.preferredhotels.com
800.323.7500 U.S.A./Canada
00.800.3237.5001 Europe (UIFN)
Other areas: See page 192

THE LANDMARK LONDON

The Landmark London is truly one of the world's leading hotels. Offering some of the largest guestrooms in London, it is an oasis of peace and serenity in the heart of the capital. Located in fashionable Marylebone, the new Notting Hill, The Landmark London sits with the famous West End on its doorstep. Heathrow Int'l. Airport: 15 miles/24 km, 15 minutes, via Heathrow Express train.

ACCOMMODATIONS: 299 total guestrooms, including 47 suites, each with three multi-line phones, data port, voice mail, VCR/DVD on request, newspaper, safe, mini-bar, robes, hair dryer and marble bathrooms.

FACILITIES/SERVICES: E'SPA treatments and massages, 50-foot (15-meter) pool, spa, sauna, steam room and salon.

BUSINESS SERVICES: Secretarial and translating services available.

DINING: The Michelin two-star "John Burton-Race at The Landmark," with French haute cuisine; the spectacular "Winter Garden," famous for its award-winning afternoon tea and exquisite setting; or enjoy a relaxed meal in the traditional "Cellars Bar and Restaurant."

MEETINGS: Total Meeting Rooms: 11 Total Sq. Ft.: 16,815 / Sq. M.: 1,565

RATES: GBP 330.00 to 1,565.00; Corporate, Group, Package rates.

Mr. Francis Green, General Manager

---

222 Marylebone Road
London NW1 6JQ, United Kingdom
Tel: +44.207.631.8000
Fax: +44.207.631.8080
Email: reservations@thelandmark.co.uk
www.landmarklondon.co.uk

Worldwide Reservations
www.preferredhotels.com
800.323.7500 U.S.A./Canada
00.800.3237.5001 Europe (UIFN)
Other areas: See page 192

THE LANESBOROUGH

ACCOMMODATIONS: 95 total guestrooms, each with three phones (two with multiple lines), data port, high-speed Internet access, voice mail, VCR on request, DVD player, newspaper, fax machine, CD player, safe, mini-bar, robes, hair dryer. Complimentary in-room computer with Internet access, video and music libraries. Complimentary 24-hour butler service.

FACILITIES/SERVICES: Fitness studio, concierge, shoe shine, child care services, dry cleaning and florist.

BUSINESS SERVICES: On-site Business Center, secretarial and translating services.

DINING: "The Conservatory" offers innovative cuisine, featuring Pacific Rim and Mediterranean flavors. The "Library" and "Withdrawing Room" are available for drinks in a traditional English club setting.

MEETINGS: Total Meeting Rooms: 6
Total Sq. Ft.: 5,210 / Sq. M.: 494

RATES: GBP 275.00 to 5,000.00; Group, Package rates.

Mr. Geoffrey A. Gelardi,
V.P. & Managing Director

Hyde Park Corner
London SW1X 7TA, United Kingdom
Tel: +44.20.7259.5599
Fax: +44.20.7259.5606
Email: info@lanesborough.com
www.lanesborough.com

London's foremost address in the heart of the capital, The Lanesborough captures the gracious style and warm hospitality of a Regency residence. A retreat to a bygone era of regal sophistication. Standing on Hyde Park Corner in prestigious Knightsbridge. Near to Buckingham Palace and Harrods. Heathrow Int'l. Airport: 14 miles/20 km, 45 minutes.

Worldwide Reservations
www.preferredhotels.com
800.323.7500 U.S.A./Canada
00.800.3237.5001 Europe (UIFN)
Other areas: See page 192

ST ANDREWS BAY GOLF RESORT & SPA

ACCOMMODATIONS: 209 total guestrooms, including 17 suites, each with voice mail, data port, high-speed Internet access, CD and DVD player, newspaper, robes, hair dryer, mini-bar, iron & board and in-house movies.

FACILITIES/SERVICES: Two magnificent championship golf courses with cliff-edged tees and greens. European-style spa indulges both body and soul.

BUSINESS SERVICES: Business Center. Secretarial services available.

DINING: Formal dining in the airy environment of "The Squire." "Kittock's Den" provides a cozy, seductive setting with light fare. "The Clubhouse" with its panoramic scenery offers an intimate dining experience serving fresh local seafood. Opening 2003, "Esperante," is an elegant Tuscan-influenced fine dining restaurant.

MEETINGS: Total Meeting Rooms: 15 Total Sq. Ft.: 15,000 / Sq. M.: 1,396

RATES: GBP 160.00 to 230.00; Corporate, Group, Package rates.

Mr. Stephen Carter,
General Manager

St Andrews
Fife KY16 8PN, United Kingdom
Tel: +44.1.334.837000
Fax: +44.1.334.471115
Email: info@standrewsbay.com
www.standrewsbay.com

St Andrews Bay Golf Resort & Spa is Scotland's newest hotel that sits proudly amidst the rugged, coastal landscape of the North Sea while commanding spectacular views of medieval St Andrews. The Resort offers meticulous attention to detail in the comfort of a modern world-class resort located at the "Home of Golf." St Andrews Bay is just 1.5 miles from downtown St Andrews. The Resort is surrounded by the rolling landscape of the Kingdom of Fife. Leuchars train station: 7 miles/11 km. Edinburgh Int'l. Airport: 50 miles/80 km, 50 minutes.

Worldwide Reservations
www.preferredhotels.com
800.323.7500 U.S.A./Canada
00.800.3237.5001 Europe (UIFN)
Other areas: See page 192

AFRICA

PALMERAIE GOLF PALACE & RESORT

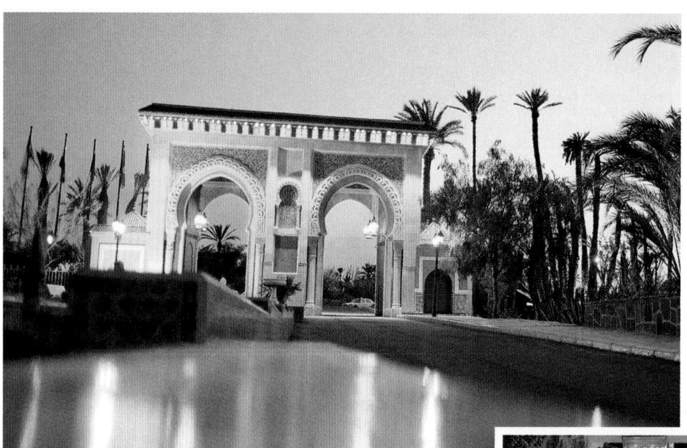

This unique palace built in the traditional Marrakchi style, is a door opened on the Moroccan culture and architecture. Relax in this luxurious resort nestled in a legendary palm grove. Experience a warm and friendly atmosphere in a peaceful and elegant place. 10 minutes away from the city center, in the protected palm grove of Marrakech. This deluxe hotel is surrounded by a beautiful 18-hole golf course designed by Robert Trent Jones, Sr. Menara Marrakech Airport: 9 miles/15 km, 15 minutes.

Worldwide Reservations
www.preferredhotels.com
800.323.7500 U.S.A./Canada
00.800.3237.5001 Europe (UIFN)
Other areas: See page 192

ACCOMMODATIONS: 314 total guestrooms, including 28 suites, each with two phones, newspaper, safe, mini-bar, robes, hair dryer and bottled water.

FACILITIES/SERVICES: Sauna, hammam, Jacuzzi, spa, concierge services, shoe shine, fitness center, child care services, salon, tennis, dry cleaning, shops, horseback riding, squash and 18-hole golf course.

BUSINESS SERVICES: On-site business center, secretarial services, and translating services on request. Registered address and office rental available.

DINING: The hotel offers ten restaurants and four bars, and discotheque for your dining pleasure.

MEETINGS: Total Meeting Rooms: 16
Total Sq. Ft.: 17,426 / Sq. M.: 1,619

RATES: MAD 2,900.00 to 3,800.00; Corporate, Group, Package rates.

Mr. Marc Saunier,
General Manager

Les Jardins de la Palmeraie, B.P. 1488
Marrakech, Morocco
Tel: +212.44.30.10.10
Fax: +212.44.30.50.50
+212.44.30.90.00
Email: reservation@pgp.ma
www.pgpmarrakech.com

FANCOURT HOTEL & COUNTRY CLUB ESTATE

Fancourt offers a combination of old-world charm and contemporary luxury on 1,137 acres (515 hectares) of lush countryside with the Outeniqua Mountains as its backdrop. Guests will cherish each moment in this haven of tranquility and style. Situated in the heart of the Garden Route. George Airport: 4.3 miles/7 km, 7 minutes. Cape Town Airport: 260 miles/420 km, 4 hours.

ACCOMMODATIONS: 150 total guestrooms, including 85 suites, each with two phones, voice mail, mini-bar, newspaper, safe, robes, tea/coffee, Internet connection and hair dryer. VCR on request.

FACILITIES/SERVICES: Four Gary Player courses including the exciting new Links course (host to the President's Cup 2003), Golf Academy, tennis courts, snooker room, fitness center, spa, child care services, dry cleaning, shoe shine, salon, swimming pools, lawn bowling, cinema and walking trail.

BUSINESS SERVICES: Business Center, secretarial and translating services.

DINING: Italian in "La Cantina," healthy cuisine in the "Morning Glory," seafood in "Le Pêcheur" and fusion cuisine in "Bramble Lodge."

MEETINGS: Total Meeting Rooms: 7
Total Sq. Ft.: 11,840 / Sq. M.: 1,102

RATES: ZAR 1,540.00 to 6,175.00; Corporate, Group, Package rates.

Mr. Steven Thielke,
Hotel General Manager

Montagu Street, Blanco, P.O. Box 2266
George 6530, South Africa
Tel: +27.44.804.0000
Fax: +27.44.804.0700
Email: hotel@fancourt.co.za
www.fancourt.com

Worldwide Reservations
www.preferredhotels.com
800.323.7500 U.S.A./Canada
00.800.3237.5001 Europe (UIFN)
Other areas: See page 192

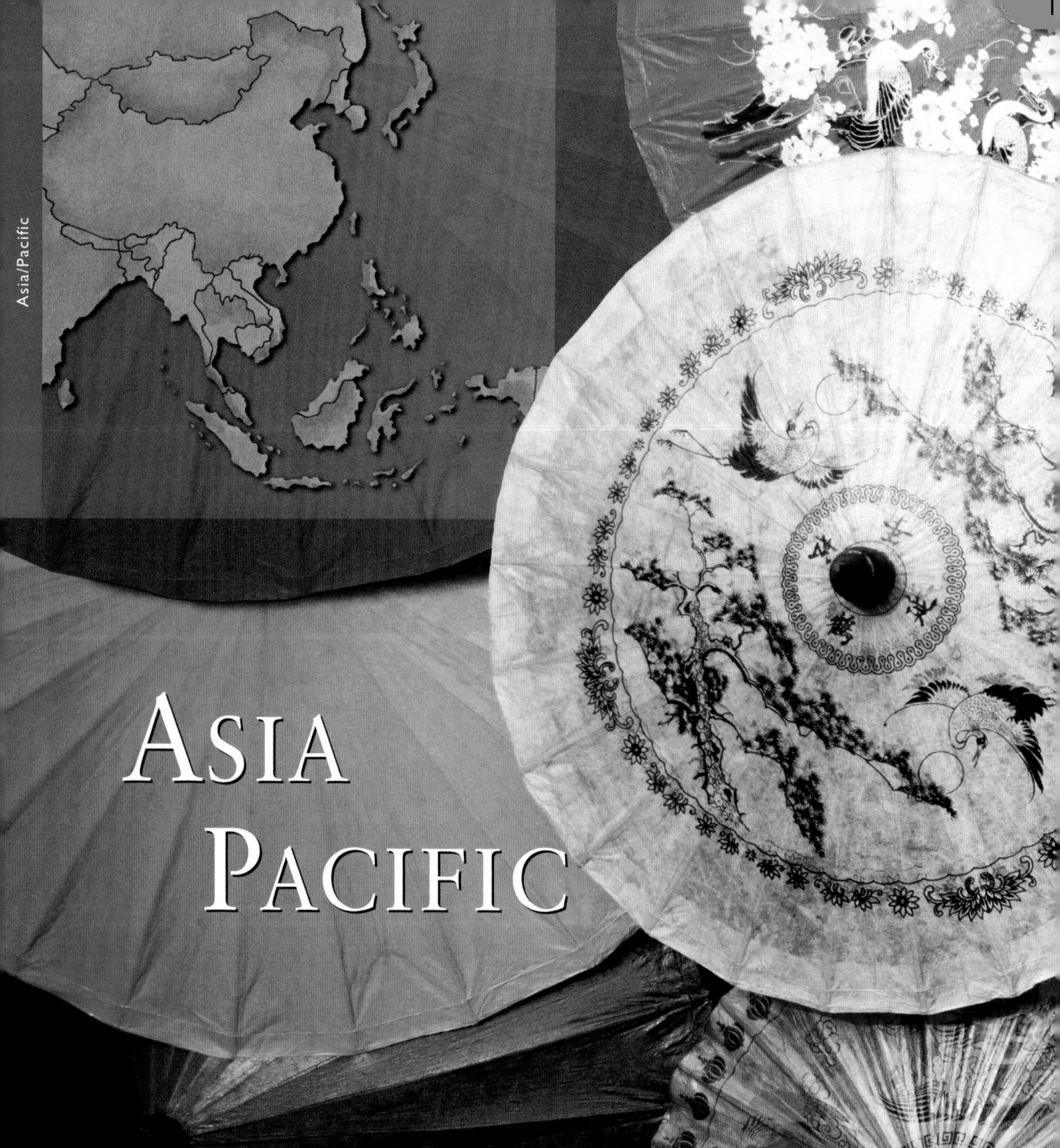
Asia/Pacific
ASIA
PACIFIC

RAFFLES HOTEL LE ROYAL

Opened in 1929 in buildings that are an inspired blend of Khmer, Art Deco and French architecture, and recently restored in the spirit of a tropical palatial residence, Raffles Hotel Le Royal occupies an entire city block and is set amidst fragrant tropical gardens. Guests can refresh their spirits at this charming, historic hotel. Located in the heart of the city of Phnom Penh. Pochentong Int'l. Airport: 6 miles/10 km, 20 minutes.

ACCOMMODATIONS: 210 total guestrooms, including 21 suites, each with phones, voice mail, newspaper, safe, mini-bar and robes.

FACILITIES/SERVICES: Spa, pool, fitness center, dry cleaning, shoe shine, salon and the "Sugar Palm Club" for children.

BUSINESS SERVICES: On-site Business Center, secretarial and translating services, Internet access.

DINING: Guests can choose from eight distinctive restaurants and bars featuring a variety of cuisines that will satisfy the most discriminating palates.

MEETINGS: Total Meeting Rooms: 5 Total Sq. Ft.: 5,382 / Sq. M.: 501

RATES: USD 260.00 to 2,000.00; Corporate, Group, Package rates.

Mr. Gilbert Madhavan,
Area General Manager

---

92 Rukhak Vithei Dawn Penh, off Monivong Blvd.
Phnom Penh, Cambodia
Tel: +855.23.981.888
Fax: +855.23.981.168
Email: emailus.leroyal@raffles.com
www.raffles.com

Worldwide Reservations
www.preferredhotels.com
800.323.7500 U.S.A./Canada
00.800.3237.5001 Europe (UIFN)
Other areas: See page 192

RAFFLES GRAND HOTEL D'ANGKOR

ACCOMMODATIONS: 131 total guestrooms, including 12 suites, each with voice mail, satellite TV, newspaper, safe, mini-bar and robes. VCR on request.

FACILITIES/SERVICES: Exercise course, tennis, spa, fitness center, concierge, child care services, dry cleaning, shoe shine and shops.

BUSINESS SERVICES: On-site Business Center, secretarial and translating services, Internet access.

DINING: Guests may choose from any of Raffles Grand Hotel d'Angkor's restaurants and bars with cuisine ranging from Royal Khmer to International choices.

RATES: USD 310.00 to 1,900.00; Corporate, Group, Package rates.

Mr. Gilbert Madhavan,
Area General Manager

---

1 Vithei Charles De Gaulle, Khum Svay Dang Kum
Siem Reap, Cambodia
Tel: +855.6.396.3888
Fax: +855.6.396.3168
Email: emailus.grandhoteldangkor@raffles.com
www.raffles.com

Raffles Grand Hotel D'Angkor is a historic landmark resort with traditional Cambodian hospitality in a romantic garden setting. This is an oasis for travelers who seek great style, history and quality. Located in the center of Siem Reap with 646,000 square feet (60,000 square meters) of beautifully landscaped gardens. Five miles (eight kilometers) from the famed Angkor complex. Siem Reap Airport: 4 miles/7 km, 15 minutes.

Worldwide Reservations
www.preferredhotels.com
800.323.7500 U.S.A./Canada
00.800.3237.5001 Europe (UIFN)
Other areas: *See page 192*

THE IMPERIAL, NEW DELHI

Built in 1931 as the most luxurious hotel in New Delhi, The Imperial showcases a unique blend of Victorian, old Colonial and informal Art Deco. Among Asia's finest hotels, The Imperial, spread over sprawling gardens, offers a unique experience embracing history and modern conveniences. An oasis of calm in the hectic rush of modern living, the hotel is located in the exclusive commercial and shopping district of Connaught Place near the President's estate, museums, monuments and parks. Indira Gandhi Int'l. Airport: 20 miles/32 km, 30 minutes.

Worldwide Reservations

www.preferredhotels.com

800.323.7500 U.S.A./Canada

00.800.3237.5001 Europe (UIFN)

Other areas: See page 192

ACCOMMODATIONS: 230 total guestrooms, including 45 suites, each with two phones, Internet access, voice mail, newspaper, fax machine, CD player, safe, mini-bar, robes and hair dryer.

FACILITIES/SERVICES: Spa, fitness center, concierge, shoe shine, salon, dry cleaning and children's amenities/services.

BUSINESS SERVICES: Business Center, secretarial services, translating services, and a printing and binding facility.

DINING: "The Spice Route" – voted one of the top 10 restaurants in the world by *Condé Nast Traveler.* "1911 Restaurant & Bar" – with culinary fare from the crossroads of the world. "Daniell's Tavern – A Raj Legacy" traces a culinary journey in the footsteps of painters Thomas and William Daniell. "San Gimignano – Romancing Italia" is an Italian restaurant.

MEETINGS: Total Meeting Rooms: 3
Total Sq. Ft.: 6,771 / Sq. M.: 677

RATES: USD 250.00 to 1,100.00; Corporate, Group, Package rates.

Mr. Pierre Jochem, Vice President & General Manager

Janpath
New Delhi 110001, India
Tel: +91.11.3341234
Fax: +91.11.3342255
Email: luxury@theimperialindia.com
www.theimperialindia.com

GOODWOOD PARK HOTEL

ACCOMMODATIONS: 235 total guestrooms, including 117 suites, each with coffee and tea, data port, voice mail, newspaper, safe, mini-bar and robes. Some rooms with VCR.

FACILITIES/SERVICES: Fitness center, concierge, pools, child care service, dry cleaning, shoe shine, salon, florist, foot reflexology salon, spa and cake shop.

BUSINESS SERVICES: Business Center, secretarial and translating services available.

DINING: "Gordon Grill" for continental cuisine, "Chang Jiang" for Shanghai cooking, "Shima" for Japanese cuisine, "Garden" for seafood, "Min Jiang" for Sichuan, "Café L'Espresso" for English high tea, "Coffee Lounge" for international and local cuisines, and "SOL" for Spanish cuisine.

MEETINGS: Total Meeting Rooms: 5
Total Sq. Ft.: 4,584 / Sq. M.: 426

RATES: SGD 385.00 to 3,000.00; Corporate, Group, Package rates.

Mrs. Mavis Oei, Deputy Chairman/General Manager

---

22 Scotts Road
Singapore 228221, Singapore
Tel: +65.6737.7411
Fax: +65.6732.8558
Email:
enquiries@goodwoodparkhotel.com.sg
www.goodwoodparkhotel.com.sg

A national landmark that recalls the splendor of the colonial era, the Goodwood Park is one of Asia's grand hotels and a tranquil oasis in the bustling city of Singapore. Goodwood Park offers the cozy and luxurious accommodations that reflect the familiar comforts of home. Conveniently located in one of the most prestigious addresses in town, the Goodwood Park Hotel is located on the fringes of the Orchard Road and Scotts Road entertainment district. Changi Int'l. Airport: 12 miles/ 20 km, 25 minutes.

Worldwide Reservations
www.preferredhotels.com
800.323.7500 U.S.A./Canada
00.800.3237.5001 Europe (UIFN)
Other areas: See page 192

RAFFLES HOTEL

Established in 1887, Raffles Hotel is one of the few remaining grand hotels in the world. With its unique blend of tropical garden settings and classical architecture, the hotel is the legendary symbol for all the "fables of the exotic East." Together with its rich accommodations, Raffles offers all the luxurious amenities of a truly grand hotel. Located in the heart of Singapore's business and historic district, just a two-minute MRT train ride from Orchard Road. Changi Int'l Airport: 14 miles/22 km, 20 minutes.

Worldwide Reservations

www.preferredhotels.com

800.323.7500 U.S.A./Canada

00.800.3237.5001 Europe (UIFN)

Other areas: See page 192

ACCOMMODATIONS: 103 suites, each with two multi-line phones, data port, voice mail, newspaper, safe, robes, service call button for personal butler. VCR on request.

FACILITIES/SERVICES: 24-hour swimming pool and fitness center, spa, child care services, dry cleaning, salon, florist, 24-hour personal butler, doctor, shops, museum, cooking school and theatre.

BUSINESS SERVICES: On-site Business Center, secretarial and translating services available.

DINING: Choose from 19 distinctive award-winning restaurants and bars serving the finest fare of the East, from renowned traditional tiffin curries to continental specialties. Also the "Long Bar," where the famous Singapore Sling was created.

MEETINGS: Total Meeting Rooms: 7
Total Sq. Ft.: 16,609 / Sq. M.: 1,546

RATES: SGD 650.00 to 4,000.00

Mr. Javier Rosenberg,
General Manager

---

1 Beach Road
Singapore 189673, Singapore
Tel: +65.6337.1886
Fax: +65.6339.7650
Email: raffles@raffles.com
www.raffleshotel.com

M
MIKIMOTO®
NEW YORK BEVERLY HILLS SOUTH COAST PLAZA LAS VEGAS
TOKYO LONDON PARIS TOLL FREE 1 888 701 2323
WWW.MIKIMOTOAMERICA.COM

MAXSTUDIO.COM

MEETING PLANNING INFORMATION

■ AMERICAS

	Maximum Group Block	Total Square Feet	Total Square Meters	Front Screen Projection	Rear Screen Projection	Theater Capacity	Reception Capacity	Banquet Capacity	U-Shape Capacity	Boardroom Capacity
Gran Estanplaza São Paulo São Paulo, Brazil	50	9,688	900	120	120	250	250	140	60	70
Metropolitan Hotel, Vancouver Vancouver, British Columbia, Canada	100	7,800	726	80	70	150	250	120	40	40
Hotel Grand Pacific Victoria, British Columbia, Canada	150	12,000	1,117	180	160	300	300	240	78	48
Metropolitan Hotel, Toronto Toronto, Ontario, Canada	250	13,000	1,210	180	80	360	360	300	60	30
Soho Metropolitan Toronto, Ontario, Canada	40	2,230	208	37	17	108	108	90	46	44
Royal Capri Resort & Spa Playa del Carmen, Quintana Roo, Mexico	200	8,400	780	250	250	500	600	350	50	35
The Wynfrey Hotel at Riverchase Galleria Birmingham, Alabama, United States	300	30,000	2,793	560	400	1,200	1,200	800		45
Hotel Captain Cook Anchorage, Alaska, United States	350	18,507	1,723	500	500	1,250	1,000	770	48	40
The Peabody Little Rock Little Rock, Arkansas, United States	350	40,000	3,724	1,000	900	1,200	1,200	900	40	30
Quail Lodge Resort & Golf Club Carmel, California, United States	97	8,301	773	200	200	300	300	200	40	40
Surf & Sand Resort Laguna Beach, California, United States	165	10,000	931	170	130	277	263	208	65	40
The Balboa Bay Club Resort and Spa Newport Beach, California, United States	100	15,464	1,440	360	275	650	750	540		
Miramonte Resort, Indian Wells Palm Springs/Indian Wells, California, United States	200	14,000	1,303	225	175	525	700	325	64	12
Rancho Bernardo Inn San Diego, California, United States	270	15,000	1,396	300	270	500	500	400	60	90
La Valencia Hotel San Diego/La Jolla, California, United States	80	5,000	466	70		140	200	150	45	34
The Huntington Hotel & Nob Hill Spa San Francisco, California, United States		1,800	168	30	30	50	65	50	30	14
Hotel Valencia Santana Row San Jose, California, United States	150	3,804	354		114	206	285	168	60	46
Bacara Resort & Spa Santa Barbara, California, United States	220	35,000	3,259	770	600	1,250	1,175	920	105	16
Vineyard Creek Hotel, Spa and Conference Center Santa Rosa/Sonoma County, California, United States	150	21,000	1,955	700	600	800	1,100	700	500	24
The Pines Lodge Beaver Creek, Colorado, United States	72	3,145	293	130	100	100	250	150	45	48
The Broadmoor Colorado Springs, Colorado, United States	650	110,000	10,241	1,100	1,000	1,800	3,000	1,250		4
The Brown Palace Hotel Denver, Colorado, United States	150	15,000	1,396	320	425	850	1,000	500	60	14
Keystone Lodge Keystone, Colorado, United States	152	100,000	9,310	1,275	1,275	2,250	2,066	1,848	1,254	16
The Lodge at Vail Vail, Colorado, United States	120	9,269	863	258	230	350	500	290	120	12

MEETING PLANNING INFORMATION

■ AMERICAS cont'd

Hotel	Maximum Group Block	Total Square Feet	Total Square Meters	Front Screen Projection	Rear Screen Projection	Theater Capacity	Reception Capacity	Banquet Capacity	U-Shape Capacity	Boardroom Capacity
Hotel George Washington, D.C., United States	75	2,488	232	54	50	100	200	80	46	48
Washington Terrace Hotel Washington, D.C., United States	150	6,700	624	100	100	220	200	150		14
Hotel du Pont Wilmington, Delaware, United States	100	30,000	2,793	250	150	500	600	400		30
Amelia Island Plantation Inn Amelia Island, Florida, United States	240	49,000	4,562	600	500	1,000	1,000	744	65	30
The Lodge & Club at Ponte Vedra Beach Jacksonville, Florida, United States	150	5,680	529	100	72	200	200	156	55	66
Marco Beach Ocean Resort™ Marco Island/Naples, Florida, United States	50	950	88	25		25	24	24	22	12
Mayfair House Hotel Miami/Coconut Grove, Florida, United States	160	12,000	1,117	220	170	300	500	200	60	20
The Peabody Orlando Orlando, Florida, United States	750	57,000	5,307	1,800		3,000	3,050	2,420	69	16
Celebration Hotel Orlando/Celebration, Florida, United States	90	5,000	466	85	65	175	150	130	50	12
Brazilian Court Hotel Palm Beach, Florida, United States	40	1,872	174	75	50	75	150	110	46	10
The Casa Monica Hotel St. Augustine, Florida, United States	138	15,000	1,396	225	125	325	400	225	40	12
Château Élan Winery & Resort Atlanta/Braselton, Georgia, United States	290	38,000	3,538	375	375	650	750		130	
Halekulani Honolulu, Hawaii, United States	125	8,454	787	200	180	400	500	320	40	30
Mauna Lani Bay Hotel & Bungalows Kohala Coast, Hawaii, United States	175	7,800	726	280	280	400	350	325	150	150
The Peninsula Chicago Chicago, Illinois, United States	150	19,000	1,769	230	160	375	600	300	64	14
Canterbury Hotel Indianapolis, Indiana, United States	75	2,673	249	40	40	85	150	110	30	12
Le Pavillon Hotel New Orleans, Louisiana, United States	150	9,063	844	135	100	200	350	200	50	12
Harbor Court Hotel Baltimore, Maryland, United States	125	7,700	717	150	100	300	275	175	66	16
The Inn at Perry Cabin St. Michaels, Maryland, United States	41	4,434	413	120		140	180	144	60	60
Boston Harbor Hotel Boston, Massachusetts, United States	150	15,000	1,396	150	100	400	500	350	60	40
Fifteen Beacon Boston, Massachusetts, United States	20	1,175	109				70	40		20
The Charles Hotel, Harvard Square Boston/Cambridge, Massachusetts, United States	250	13,300	1,209	275	225	525	600	325	60	10
Wequassett Inn Resort and Golf Club Cape Cod/Chatham, Massachusetts, United States	104	6,120	570	153	153	281	320	250	71	25
The Orchards Hotel Williamstown, Massachusetts, United States	30	2,700	251	100	136	170	225	170	80	50

MEETING PLANNING INFORMATION

■ AMERICAS cont'd

Hotel	Maximum Group Block	Total Square Feet	Total Square Meters	Front Screen Projection	Rear Screen Projection	Theater Capacity	Reception Capacity	Banquet Capacity	U-Shape Capacity	Boardroom Capacity
The Townsend Hotel Detroit/Birmingham, Michigan, United States	150	9,300	866	380	210	450	550	380	100	18
The Grand Hotel Minneapolis Minneapolis/St. Paul, Minnesota, United States	80	8,000	745	200	150	300	500	400	75	25
Hotel Phillips Kansas City, Missouri, United States	215	5,668	528	100		150	170	120	30	14
Clayton On The Park, A Hotel & Residence St. Louis, Missouri, United States	30	10,833	1,009	30		40	175	56	15	10
Inn of the Anasazi Santa Fe, New Mexico, United States	59	825	77	30		40	80	40	23	28
The Sagamore Bolton Landing, New York, United States	350	26,000	2,421	564	564	1,000	1,000	600	72	36
The Garden City Hotel Long Island, New York, United States	200	25,000	2,323	325	275	650	650	500	125	75
The St. Regis New York New York City, New York, United States	100	15,185	1,414	200	150	300	500	300	50	50
Ballantyne Resort Charlotte, North Carolina, United States	175	16,000	1,490	280	280	800	600	400	200	14
The Park Hotel Charlotte, North Carolina, United States	192	8,102	754	170	100	350	350	152	80	12
The Cincinnatian Hotel Cincinnati, Ohio, United States	50	3,157	294	60	60	120	125	90	42	45
The Heathman Hotel Portland, Oregon, United States	60	3,495	325	60		90	140	120	30	15
The Hotel Hershey® Hershey, Pennsylvania, United States	220	22,000	2,048	250	186	500	700	360	60	64
The Rittenhouse Hotel Philadelphia, Pennsylvania, United States	70	8,470	787	276	264	400	600	400	70	100
Charleston Place Charleston, South Carolina, United States	300	33,000	3,072	860	650	1,400	1,700	1,100	80	14
The Peabody Memphis Memphis, Tennessee, United States	375	80,000	7,448	600	600	2,100	2,200	1,350	200	
The Hermitage Hotel Nashville, Tennessee, United States	65	5,271	491	138		280	300	230	80	60
Hotel Derek Houston, Texas, United States	200	10,250	954	330	280	550	500	420	75	50
The Houstonian Hotel, Club & Spa Houston, Texas, United States	200	33,000	3,072	350	275	625	700	525	60	80
La Mansión del Rio San Antonio, Texas, United States	250	15,000	1,396	280	200	450	500	330	86	14
Stein Eriksen Lodge Park City, Utah, United States	170	5,500	512	275	275	440	418	328		14
Topnotch at Stowe Resort & Spa Stowe, Vermont, United States	100	10,000	931	140	70	200	300	200	68	22
Keswick Hall at Monticello Charlottesville, Virginia, United States	48	7,970	742	90	70	200	200	120	48	26
The Jefferson Hotel Richmond, Virginia, United States	150	26,000	2,421	250	225	500	500	320	75	10

MEETING PLANNING INFORMATION

■ AMERICAS cont'd

	Maximum Group Block	Total Square Feet	Total Square Meters	Front Screen Projection	Rear Screen Projection	Theater Capacity	Reception Capacity	Banquet Capacity	U-Shape Capacity	Boardroom Capacity
Kingsmill Resort Williamsburg, Virginia, United States	350	16,000	1,490	340	225	570	610	450	72	26
Semiahmoo Resort Blaine, Washington, United States	198	22,000	2,048	420	320	600	600	360	50	14
Sorrento Hotel Seattle, Washington, United States	50	4,000	372	44	24	80	120	80	34	36
The Woodmark Hotel on Lake Washington Seattle/Kirkland, Washington, United States	35	4,936	460	80	50	190	200	180	40	14
Willows Lodge Seattle/Woodinville, Washington, United States	40	4,000	372	100	80	180	180	180	60	50
The Davenport Hotel Spokane, Washington, United States		25,000	2,328							
The Greenbrier® White Sulphur Springs, West Virginia, United States		85,000	7,914	800	800	1,500		1,200	60	50
The Pfister Hotel Milwaukee, Wisconsin, United States	250	25,000	2,323	450	350	1,050	1,500	900	65	20
Snake River Lodge & Spa Jackson Hole, Wyoming, United States	80	4,041	376	150	25	200	250	150	60	40

■ CARRIBEAN

	Maximum Group Block	Total Square Feet	Total Square Meters	Front Screen Projection	Rear Screen Projection	Theater Capacity	Reception Capacity	Banquet Capacity	U-Shape Capacity	Boardroom Capacity
Sandy Lane St. James, Barbados		8,000	745	30	30	48	60	35	35	60
Peter Island Resort Tortola, British Virgin Islands	52	900	84	30		60	100	100	15	14

■ EUROPE

	Maximum Group Block	Total Square Feet	Total Square Meters	Front Screen Projection	Rear Screen Projection	Theater Capacity	Reception Capacity	Banquet Capacity	U-Shape Capacity	Boardroom Capacity
Anassa Latchi, Cyprus	80	10,680	994	165	165	500	800	270	50	20
The Annabelle Pafos, Cyprus	90	7,158	666	260	260	400	400	300	50	50
Hotel Palace Praha Prague, Czech Republic	80	3,950	368			80		50	33	26
La Trémoille Paris, France	25	646	60	15		25	30	20	20	20
Montalembert Paris, France	30	398	37							
Hotel Bayerischer Hof Munich, Germany	200	48,935	4,556	550	550	1,500	3,000	1,415	180	100
Dromoland Castle Hotel County Clare, Ireland	100	5,088	474	320	320	450	600	320	70	90
The K Club Dublin/Kildare, Ireland		4,844	451	40	40	70	200	160		30
Aghadoe Heights Hotel Killarney, County Kerry, Ireland		2,861	266			120	120	80	30	30
Palazzo Arzaga Hotel, Spa & Golf Resort Brescia/Verona, Italy	60	3,918	365	180	180	250	300	200	30	18
Excelsior Palace Hotel Rapallo/Portofino Coast, Italy		6,997	650	230	170	450	450	330	70	30

MEETING PLANNING INFORMATION

■ EUROPE cont'd

Hotel	Maximum Group Block	Total Square Feet	Total Square Meters	Front Screen Projection	Rear Screen Projection	Theater Capacity	Reception Capacity	Banquet Capacity	U-Shape Capacity	Boardroom Capacity
Palazzo Sasso Ravello, Italy	44	1,033	96	35	35	50	50	50	35	35
Hotel de Russie Rome, Italy	40	2,225	207	57		90	100	60	36	36
San Clemente Palace Venice, Italy	100	5,791	538	196	196	315	350	270	129	60
Grand Hotel Huis ter Duin Amsterdam/Noordwijk aan Zee, The Netherlands	220	41,505	3,864	500	480	1,050	1,050	790	150	170
The San Roque Club Cadiz/San Roque, Spain	50	689	64	30	30	60	150	100	30	40
Beau-Rivage, Geneva Geneva, Switzerland	30	5,522	514	120	120	300	650	300	80	40
Grand Hotel National Lucerne, Switzerland	15	6,302	587	110	110	200	550	270	50	50
Park Hotel Vitznau Lucerne/Vitznau, Switzerland	80	1,560	145	80	40	130	150	200	45	45
The Carlton Hotel St. Moritz, Switzerland	105	4,844	451	110	110	180	200	160	50	50
Grand Hotel Zermatterhof Zermatt, Switzerland	50	5,400	503	200	180	280	350	250		
Blakes Hotel London, United Kingdom	12	344	32			34	50	34	30	34
The Landmark London London, United Kingdom	150	16,815	1,565	190	162	380	500	408	40	40
The Lanesborough London, United Kingdom	40	5,210	494	70	55	120	250	120	60	70
St Andrews Bay Golf Resort & Spa St Andrews, Scotland, United Kingdom	217	15,000	1,396	420	420	677	700	504	112	168

■ AFRICA

Hotel	Maximum Group Block	Total Square Feet	Total Square Meters	Front Screen Projection	Rear Screen Projection	Theater Capacity	Reception Capacity	Banquet Capacity	U-Shape Capacity	Boardroom Capacity
Palmeraie Golf Palace & Resort Marrakech, Morocco		17,426	1,619			100	1,200	450	160	250
Fancourt Hotel & Country Club Estate George, South Africa	150	11,840	1,102	326	160	670	595	452	146	181

■ ASIA

Hotel	Maximum Group Block	Total Square Feet	Total Square Meters	Front Screen Projection	Rear Screen Projection	Theater Capacity	Reception Capacity	Banquet Capacity	U-Shape Capacity	Boardroom Capacity
Raffles Hotel Le Royal Phnom Penh, Cambodia	100	5,382	501	225	225	430	630	300	120	255
Raffles Grand Hotel D'Angkor Siem Reap, Cambodia										
The Imperial, New Delhi New Delhi, India	30	6,771	677	150	120	350	400	175	90	90
Goodwood Park Hotel Singapore, Singapore	50	4,584	426	120		320	500	300	45	48
Raffles Hotel Singapore, Singapore	50	16,609	1,546	180	100	400	400	260	54	38

RESORT AMENITIES & SPAS

■ AMERICAS

	Spa	Golf	Tennis	Health Club	Pool	Beach	Boating	Scuba Diving	Snorkeling	Wind Surfing	Horseback Riding	Fishing	Jogging	Snow Skiing
Hotel Grand Pacific Victoria, British Columbia, Canada	●	❍	❍	●	●	❍	❍	❍	❍	❍		❍	❍	
Soho Metropolitan Toronto, Ontario, Canada	●	❍	❍	●	●	❍	❍						❍	❍
Royal Capri Resort & Spa Playa del Carmen, Quintana Roo, Mexico	●	❍	●	●	●	●	●	●	●	●	❍	❍	●	
The Wynfrey Hotel at Riverchase Galleria Birmingham, Alabama, United States	●	❍		●	●							❍	●	
The Peabody Little Rock Little Rock, Arkansas, United States		❍	❍	●			❍				❍	❍		
Quail Lodge Resort & Golf Club Carmel, California, United States	●	●	●	●	●	●	❍	❍	❍	❍	❍	●	●	
Surf & Sand Resort Laguna Beach, California, United States	●	❍			●	●	❍		❍			❍	❍	
The Balboa Bay Club Resort and Spa Newport Beach, California, United States	●	❍	❍	●	●	●	●	❍	❍	❍	❍	❍	❍	❍
Miramonte Resort, Indian Wells Palm Springs/Indian Wells, California, United States	●	❍	❍	●	●								●	
Rancho Bernardo Inn San Diego, California, United States	●	●	●	●	●								❍	
La Valencia Hotel San Diego/La Jolla, California, United States		❍	❍	●	●									
The Huntington Hotel & Nob Hill Spa San Francisco, California, United States	●	❍	❍	●	●	❍	❍	❍	❍	❍	❍	❍	❍	❍
Hotel Valencia Santana Row San Jose, California, United States	●	❍	❍	●	●								❍	
Bacara Resort & Spa Santa Barbara, California, United States	●	●	●	●	●	●	●	❍	❍	❍	❍	❍	●	
Vineyard Creek Hotel, Spa and Conference Center Santa Rosa/Sonoma County, California, United States	●	❍	❍	●	●	❍	❍				❍	❍	●	
The Pines Lodge Beaver Creek, Colorado, United States	●	❍	❍	●	●		❍			❍	❍	❍	❍	●
The Broadmoor Colorado Springs, Colorado, United States	●	●	●	●	●						❍	❍	●	
Keystone Lodge Keystone, Colorado, United States	●	❍	●	●	●		●				❍	❍	●	❍
The Lodge at Vail Vail, Colorado, United States	❍	❍	❍	❍	●		❍				❍	❍	●	●
Amelia Island Plantation Inn Amelia Island, Florida, United States	●	●	●	●	●	●	❍	❍	❍	❍	❍	●	●	❍

● On Site ❍ Off Site

RESORT AMENITIES & SPAS

AMERICAS cont'd

	Spa	Golf	Tennis	Health Club	Pool	Beach	Boating	Scuba Diving	Snorkeling	Wind Surfing	Horseback Riding	Fishing	Jogging	Snow Skiing
The Lodge & Club at Ponte Vedra Beach Jacksonville, Florida, United States	○	○	○	●	●	●	○	○	○	○	○	○	●	○
Marco Beach Ocean Resort™ Marco Island/Naples, Florida, United States	●	●	●	●	●	●		●	●	●		●	●	
Mayfair House Hotel Miami/Coconut Grove, Florida, United States	●	○	○	○	●	○	○	○	○	○		○	●	
The Peabody Orlando Orlando, Florida, United States	●	○	●	●	●	○	○	○	○	○	○	○	●	
Celebration Hotel Orlando/Celebration, Florida, United States	○	○	○	●	●	○	○	○			○	○	●	
Brazilian Court Hotel Palm Beach, Florida, United States	●	○	○	●	●	○	○	○	○	○		○		
The Casa Monica Hotel St. Augustine, Florida, United States	●	○	●	●	●	○	○	○	○	○	○	○	●	
Château Élan Winery & Resort Atlanta/Braselton, Georgia, United States	●	●	●	●	●	○	○				○	○	●	
Halekulani Honolulu, Hawaii, United States	●	○	○	●	●	●	○	○	●	○	○	○	●	
Mauna Lani Bay Hotel & Bungalows Kohala Coast, Hawaii, United States	●	●	●	●	●	●	●	●	●	○	○	●	●	
The Inn at Perry Cabin St. Michaels, Maryland, United States	○	○	○	●	●		●					●	○	
Wequassett Inn Resort and Golf Club Cape Cod/Chatham, Massachusetts, United States	○	●	●	●	●	●	●			●	○	○	○	
The Orchards Hotel Williamstown, Massachusetts, United States	○	○	○	○	●						○	○	●	○
Inn of the Anasazi Santa Fe, New Mexico, United States	○	○	○	○	○						○	○	○	○
The Sagamore Bolton Landing, New York, United States	●	●	●	●	●	●	●	●	●	●	○	●	●	●
The St. Regis New York New York City, New York, United States	●	○	○	●	○		○				○		○	
Ballantyne Resort Charlotte, North Carolina, United States	●	○	○	●	●		○						○	
The Hotel Hershey® Hershey, Pennsylvania, United States	●	●	●	●	●								●	○
The Rittenhouse Hotel Philadelphia, Pennsylvania, United States	●	○	○	●	●						○		○	
The Houstonian Hotel, Club & Spa Houston, Texas, United States	●	○	●	●	●						○		●	

● On Site ○ Off Site

RESORT AMENITIES & SPAS

■ AMERICAS cont'd

Resort	Spa	Golf	Tennis	Health Club	Pool	Beach	Boating	Scuba Diving	Snorkeling	Wind Surfing	Horseback Riding	Fishing	Jogging	Snow Skiing
Stein Eriksen Lodge Park City, Utah, United States	●	❍	❍	●	●	❍	❍	❍	❍	❍	❍	❍	❍	●
Topnotch at Stowe Resort & Spa Stowe, Vermont, United States	●	❍	●	●	●		❍			❍	●	❍	●	❍
Keswick Hall at Monticello Charlottesville, Virginia, United States	●	●	●	●	●						❍	●	●	❍
Kingsmill Resort Williamsburg, Virginia, United States	●	●	●	●	●		❍					❍	●	
Semiahmoo Resort Blaine, Washington, United States	●	●	●	●	●	●	●				❍	●	●	❍
The Woodmark Hotel on Lake Washington Seattle/Kirkland, Washington, United States	●	❍	❍	●	❍	❍	❍	❍	❍	❍	❍	❍	●	❍
Willows Lodge Seattle/Woodinville, Washington, United States	●	❍	❍				❍				❍	❍	❍	❍
The Greenbrier® White Sulphur Springs, West Virginia, United States	●	●	●	●	●						●	●	●	❍
Snake River Lodge & Spa Jackson Hole, Wyoming, United States	●	❍	❍	●	●		❍			❍	●	❍	❍	●

■ CARRIBEAN

Resort	Spa	Golf	Tennis	Health Club	Pool	Beach	Boating	Scuba Diving	Snorkeling	Wind Surfing	Horseback Riding	Fishing	Jogging	Snow Skiing
Sandy Lane St. James, Barbados	●	●	●	●	●	●	●	●	●	●	●	●	●	
Peter Island Resort Tortola, British Virgin Islands	●	❍	●	●	●	●	●	●	●	●	❍	●	●	

■ EUROPE

Resort	Spa	Golf	Tennis	Health Club	Pool	Beach	Boating	Scuba Diving	Snorkeling	Wind Surfing	Horseback Riding	Fishing	Jogging	Snow Skiing
Anassa Latchi, Cyprus	●		●	●	●	●	●	●	●	●	❍	❍	❍	
The Annabelle Pafos, Cyprus		❍	●	●	●	●	●	●	●	●	❍	❍		
Dromoland Castle Hotel County Clare, Ireland	●	●	●	●	●	●	●	❍	❍	❍	❍	●	●	
The K Club Dublin/Kildare, Ireland			❍								❍			
Aghadoe Heights Hotel Killarney, County Kerry, Ireland		❍	●	●	●	❍	❍			❍	❍	❍	●	
Palazzo Arzaga Hotel, Spa & Golf Resort Brescia/Verona, Italy	●	●	●	●	●	❍	❍	❍		❍	❍	❍	●	
Excelsior Palace Hotel Rapallo/Portofino Coast, Italy	●	❍	❍	●	●	●	❍	❍	❍	❍	❍	❍	❍	

● On Site ❍ Off Site

RESORT AMENITIES & SPAS

	Spa	Golf	Tennis	Health Club	Pool	Beach	Boating	Scuba Diving	Snorkeling	Wind Surfing	Horseback Riding	Fishing	Jogging	Snow Skiing
■ EUROPE cont'd														
Palazzo Sasso Ravello, Italy			○		●	○	●	○	○	○	○	●	●	
Hotel de Russie Rome, Italy	●	○	○	●	●								○	
San Clemente Palace Venice, Italy	●	●	●	●	●	○	○	○		○	○	○	●	
Grand Hotel Huis ter Duin Amsterdam/Noordwijk aan Zee, The Netherlands	●	○	○	●	●	●	○			○	○		○	
The San Roque Club Cadiz/San Roque, Spain		●	●		●	○	○	○		○	●	○	●	
Grand Hotel National Lucerne, Switzerland	●	○	○	●	○	○	○	○	○	○	○	○	○	○
Park Hotel Vitznau Lucerne/Vitznau, Switzerland	○	○	●	●	●	●	●	○	○	○	○	○	●	
The Carlton Hotel St. Moritz, Switzerland	●	○	○	●	●					○	○	○	○	○
Grand Hotel Zermatterhof Zermatt, Switzerland		○	○		●						○		○	○
The Landmark London London, United Kingdom	●			●	●								○	
St Andrews Bay Golf Resort & Spa St Andrews, Scotland, United Kingdom	●	●		●	●	●	●			●	●	●	●	
■ AFRICA														
Palmeraie Golf Palace & Resort Marrakech, Morocco	○	○	○	○	○						○		○	○
Fancourt Hotel & Country Club Estate George, South Africa	●	●	●	●	●	○	○	○	○	○	○	○	●	
■ ASIA/PACIFIC														
Raffles Hotel Le Royal Phnom Penh, Cambodia	●	●	●	●	●								○	
Raffles Grand Hotel D'Angkor Siem Reap, Cambodia	●		●	●	●									
The Imperial, New Delhi New Delhi, India		○		●	●						○		●	
Goodwood Park Hotel Singapore, Singapore	●	○	○	●	●	○	○							
Raffles Hotel Singapore, Singapore	●	○	○	●	●					○			○	

● On Site ○ Off Site

THE SOURCE FOR TRAVEL & MEETING PROFESSIONALS

Preferred Hotels® & Resorts Worldwide offers 116 of the world's finest locations for meetings and business travel.

GROUP & INCENTIVE TRAVEL

As a travel or meeting professional, you can simplify your meeting planning by contacting our regional sales executive first. We provide one simple connection for facility recommendations, rates and space availability for groups requiring 10 or more rooms per night. For more than 30 years, Preferred hotels and resorts have been the sought-after destinations for a vast array of meetings, including themed incentives, sales meetings, board meetings, team building, new product introductions and annual business meetings. For additional information, contact the Preferred sales office nearest you (see list at right) or email us at sales@preferredhotels.com.

ACCESSPREFERRED WORLDWIDE ACCOUNTS

To arrange for a corporate travel account for your company's frequently visited Preferred destinations, contact our AccessPreferred Worldwide Accounts Office at +1.312.542.9245, or email us at sales@preferredhotels.com.

SALES OFFICES

North America	+1.800.786.6397 Fax: +1.312.913.5124
Italy	+39.02.6710.0886 Fax: +39.02.6671.0502
United Kingdom	+44.(0)208.232.5651 Fax: +44.(0)208.232.5682
Germany	+49.(0)897.596.7820 Fax: +49.(0)897.596.7821
Japan	+81.3.5645.8520 Fax: +81.3.3664.3301
Hong Kong	+852.2273.5096 Fax: +852.2273.5490
Australia	+61.2.9006.1230 Fax: +61.2.9006.1010

GENERAL INFORMATION

PACKAGE PLANS

Most of our hotels offer special packages designed to make even a brief stay a memorable experience. For information, rates and availability, contact the reservation office nearest you. The list of reservation offices can be found on the inside back cover, page 192.

GROUPS/MEETINGS/EVENTS

Should you need assistance with groups requiring 10 or more rooms, please contact the sales office nearest you or email us at sales@preferredhotels.com. The list of sales offices can be found on page 176.

AVAILABILITY

Preferred hotels and resorts are available through our reservation offices on a free sale basis. Each hotel's availability is continually updated so that we can provide timely, accurate reservation information.

RATES

The rates quoted in this directory are subject to change without notice. Most rates are listed in the hotel's local currency and do not include tax or service charges except where noted. Suite and special package rates are also available upon request.

RESERVATIONS

Reservations at any Preferred hotel or resort may be made through all of our reservation offices worldwide. For a list of offices and toll-free reservation numbers, refer to the inside back cover, page 192. Information and reservations may also be obtained at www.preferredhotels.com.

CONFIRMATIONS

Our reservation offices will confirm your reservation to a maximum of nine rooms. Written confirmations may be requested at the time of booking and will be sent from the office through which you made your reservation.

CHANGES & CANCELLATIONS

If it is necessary to change or cancel a confirmed reservation booked through a Preferred reservation office or computer system, please notify the originating reservation office or your travel agent as soon as possible. Reservations must be changed or canceled in the manner in which they were booked. Cancellation policies do vary between hotels. Be sure to inquire about the hotel's specific cancellation policy when making your reservation. Sufficient notice of cancellation must be given to avoid financial penalty.

GUARANTEES

Preferred will guarantee your reservation by advance deposit or credit card. The American Express® Card is the preferred method for guaranteeing your reservation, although other credit cards will also be accepted. A guaranteed reservation will be held all night. If a guaranteed reservation is not canceled according to the hotel's cancellation policy and in the manner reserved, the hotel will bill you according to the hotel's cancellation policy.

COMMISSIONS

Preferred Hotels® & Resorts Worldwide members guarantee a minimum payment of 10 percent commission from all North American, Asian/ Pacific, Caribbean hotels and 8 percent commission from European hotels. Our members pay commission on actual room revenue booked by the professional travel agent. Please call toll-free +1.877.748.2266 or +1.312.913.0400 for assistance with commission retrieval.

HOTEL INFORMATION

Descriptions and photography of each hotel or resort has been provided by the hotel or resort. Occasionally, because of management changes or renovations, services and/or facilities may change without notice. Preferred Hotels® & Resorts Worldwide nor the individual hotel or resort can be held responsible should any changes occur.

FACILITIES FOR GUESTS WITH DISABILITIES

Facilities for guests with disabilities are available at many Preferred hotels and resorts. Contact the reservation office nearest you for more information.

DIRECTORY PHOTOGRAPHY

pg. 20-21 ©Glenn Allison/Photodisc
pg. 122-123 ©Macduff Everton
pg. 126-127 ©G. Llorca/Stock Image/Panoramic Images
pg. 158-159 ©Corbis
pg. 162-163 ©Steve Petsch/Panoramic Images

DIRECTORY

2003 EDITION

PREFERRED HOTELS® & RESORTS WORLDWIDE

Chairman of the
Advisory Board . . . . David G. Benton

Managing Director . . . . Robert M. Cornell

Senior Coordinator,
Marketing Communications . . . . Catherine Hogan

Preferred Hotels® & Resorts Worldwide
Headquarters Office:
311 South Wacker Drive, Suite 1900
Chicago, Illinois 60606 U.S.A.
Tel: +1.312.913.0400 Fax: +1.312.913.0444
info@preferredhotels.com
www.preferredhotels.com

INDEX BY CITY

INDEX BY REGION

AFRICA

THE AMERICAS

INDEX BY REGION

■ ASIA•PACIFIC

■ CARIBBEAN

INDEX BY REGION

■ EUROPE

RESERVATIONS INFORMATION

For reservations at any Preferred hotel or resort, contact your travel professional or call:

THE AMERICAS

United States, Canada and Puerto Rico

1.800.323.7500

Mexico
01.800.509.0745

Colombia
989.12.0995

Chile
1.230.020.0712

EUROPE
Austria, Denmark, France, Germany, Italy, The Netherlands, Spain, Sweden, Switzerland and United Kingdom
00.800.3237.5001 (UIFN)

From all other areas of Europe, contact our United Kingdom office at: +44.(0)20.8604.2122

AFRICA/MIDDLE EAST
Contact our United Kingdom office at:
+44.(0)20.8604.2122

GDS Information
Chain Code: PH
Apollo/Galileo
Sabre/Axess/Abacus
Amadeus
Worldspan

ASIA/PACIFIC

Australia

1.800.143762

Hong Kong
800.96.3365

Japan
0120.747.755

Singapore
1.800.227.3126

Thailand
001.800.65.6587

Taiwan
00.801.651254

From all other areas of Asia/Pacific contact Preferred's United Kingdom office at: +44.(0)20.8604.2122

INTERNET RESERVATIONS
Receive instant booking confirmation for all Preferred hotels and resorts when you, or your travel professional reserve on-line. Visit Preferred's Web site for updated hotel listings and additional information on our Partnership Programs, seasonal offers and for spontaneous "On a Whim" travel specials.

www.preferredhotels.com

Preferred Hotels® & Resorts Worldwide
311 South Wacker Drive, Suite 1900
Chicago, Illinois 60606 U.S.A.
Tel: +1.312.913.0400 Fax: +1.312.913.0444
info@preferredhotels.com
www.preferredhotels.com